Examples in MATHEMATICS FOR GCSE

Intermediate Tier
Third Edition

Ewart Smith MSc

formerly Head of Mathematics Department
Tredegar Comprehensive School

Stanley Thornes (Publishers) Ltd

First published in 1988.
Second edition published in 1993.
Third edition published in 1996 by:
Stanley Thornes (Publishers) Ltd
Ellenborough House
Wellington Street
CHELTENHAM GL50 1YW
England

96 97 98 99 00 / 10 9 8 7 6 5 4 3 2 1

A catalogue record for this book is available from the British Library.

ISBN 0 7487 2765 5

Typeset in 12pt Aldine by Tech-Set, Gateshead, Tyne & Wear.
Printed and bound in Great Britain by T.J. Press (Padstow) Ltd, Padstow, Cornwall.

Contents

Preface

The aim of this book is to provide a reservoir of examples for Year 10 and Year 11 pupils studying for the intermediate tier of the GCSE examinations at Key Stage 4.

The book is divided into two parts:

PART 1 provides exercises on individual topics and forms the basis of a course for Year 10.

PART 2 consists of thirty revision papers which can be used in Year 11.

My thanks are due to my colleague Mr Allan Snelgrove BSc for checking the answers and making several useful suggestions. I am also grateful to British Railways Board for providing the timetable information on p. 215.

Ewart Smith
1996

Part 1: Exercises

Number Work

1   Write down the next two numbers in each sequence.
   (a) 3, 5, 7, 9   (b) 5, 10, 15, 20
   (c) 4, 9, 16, 25, 36   (d) 4, -8, 12, -16
   (e) 1, 0.1, 0.01, 0.001   (f) 4, 8, 16, 32, 64

2   Put the following numbers in order of size, smallest first.
   (a) 5, -8, -4, 1, 3   (b) 0.33, $\frac{1}{3}$, 0.3, $\frac{2}{5}$
   (c) $\frac{1}{2}$, $\frac{1}{4}$, $\frac{1}{3}$, $\frac{5}{12}$ (d) 3.14, 3.41, 3.04, 3.411

3   Find
   (a) $7\frac{5}{8} + 2\frac{1}{2}$ (b) $2\frac{1}{4} - 1\frac{1}{2}$
   (c) $1\frac{1}{2} \times \frac{2}{3}$ (d) $4 \div \frac{1}{2}$
   (e) $8 \div \frac{1}{3}$ (f) $5\frac{1}{4} \times \frac{5}{7}$

4   Find
   (a) $5.24 + 0.9$ (b) $3.73 - 0.91$
   (c) 3.4×0.04 (d) $2.4 \div 0.6$
   (e) $1.2(4.6 - 2.4)$ (f) $0.6(3.1 + 2.9)$

5   Estimate the value of
   (a) 98.26×2.014 (b) $49.2 \div 24.75$
   (c) 5.97×6.02 (d) $\dfrac{72.43}{8.998}$

6   Consider the number 646.488.
   (a) What is the difference in the values of the two 6 digits?
   (b) What is the difference in the values of the two 8 digits?
   (c) What is the difference in the values of the two 4 digits?

7   Write each of the following numbers
   (i) correct to the nearest 100,
  (ii) correct to 3 significant figures,
 (iii) correct to 2 decimal places.
   (a) 9217.787   (b) 95.724   (c) 416.345

8   Write each of the following numbers correct to 3 s.f.
   (a) $\sqrt{5}$ (b) $4\sqrt{3}$ (c) $\frac{7}{16}$
   (d) $\dfrac{2}{\sqrt{3}}$ (e) 2.718^2 (f) $\sqrt[3]{100}$

9   Write down the highest common factor of
   (a) 12, 18   (b) 35, 56   (c) 70, 84
   (d) 54, 72   (e) 45, 60   (f) 108, 162

10 Write down the smallest whole number that both the following numbers will divide into exactly.
    (a) 21, 28   (b) 5, 7   (c) 56, 16
    (d) 18, 24   (e) 44, 66   (f) 25, 35

11 Place the correct symbol $>$, $<$ or $=$ between each of the following pairs of numbers.
    (a) $5\frac{1}{2}$ 5.55   (b) 0.78   0.69
    (c) -0.042 -0.12 (d) -0.7 -0.81
    (e) $3\frac{3}{8}$ 3.375   (f) -1.4 $1\frac{2}{5}$

12 Many mathematicians have tried to work out a value for π. Here are some of the numbers used.

    Babylonians $3\frac{1}{8}$, Ptolemy $\frac{377}{120}$, Chung Hung $\sqrt{10}$,
    Fibonacci 3.1418 18, Duchesne $\left(\frac{39}{22}\right)^2$
    (a) Put these numbers in order of size.
    (b) Which of these numbers is closest to the value of π you get from your calculator?

13 Simplify
    (a) $-12 + 4$ (b) $-10 + (-4)$

    (c) $8 - (-3)$ (d) $\dfrac{12}{-4}$

    (e) $(-6) \times (-2)$ (f) $-15 \div 3$

    (g) $4(3 - (-5))$ (h) $\dfrac{8 \times (-4)}{-2}$

    (i) $(-2) \times (3) \times (-4)$ (j) $\dfrac{5 - (-7)}{3 \times (-2)}$

14 The first five numbers in a pattern are 1, 4, 10, 19, 31.
    (a) Which of these numbers are
         (i) odd numbers,   (ii) prime numbers?
    (b) Write down, in order, the differences between consecutive numbers.
    (c) Write down the next two numbers in the pattern.

15 Express as a single fraction
    (a) $\frac{1}{2} + \frac{1}{4} - \frac{1}{8} - \frac{1}{16} - \frac{1}{32}$ (b) $\frac{1}{3} - \frac{1}{9} + \frac{1}{27}$
    (c) $\frac{1}{2} - \frac{1}{3} + \frac{1}{4} - \frac{1}{5}$ (d) $\frac{1}{2} + \frac{2}{3} + \frac{3}{4}$
    (e) $\frac{1}{2} - \frac{2}{3} + \frac{3}{4}$ (f) $\frac{1}{2} + \frac{2}{3} - \frac{3}{4}$

16 (a) Write down two prime numbers whose sum is 14 and whose product is 33.
    (b) Write down two prime numbers whose difference is 14 and whose product is 95.

3

17 Use your calculator to find

(a) $\dfrac{9.45 \times 3.2}{2.8}$

(b) $\dfrac{5.7 \times 4.9}{133}$

(c) $\dfrac{9.36 \times 77}{11.44 \times 6.3}$

(d) $7.2^2 + 3.9^2$

(e) $8.3^2 - 4.7^2$

(f) $10.4^2 - 9.2 \times 7.1$

(g) $\dfrac{3.7^3 - 6.2^2}{4.2 + 5.8}$

18 Which of these fractions can be written as non-recurring decimals?

$$\frac{3}{11}, \frac{4}{9}, \frac{12}{5}, \frac{5}{8}, \frac{2}{3}, \frac{13}{4}$$

19 (a) Find two numbers that add up to 5.3.

(b) Find two numbers that make 12.5 when they are multiplied together.

(c) The difference between two numbers is 4.2. What could the numbers be?

(d) One whole number is divided by another whole number and the answer is 0.6. What could the numbers be?

20 One whole number is divided by another.

(a) The calculator reads

What could the numbers be?

$$\boxed{0.8888888}$$

(b) The calculator reads

What could the numbers be?

$$\boxed{0.0888888}$$

(c) The calculator reads

What could the numbers be?

$$\boxed{2.7272727}$$

(d) The calculator reads

What could the numbers be?

$$\boxed{0.0272727}$$

21 Write each of the following numbers as the sum of two prime numbers.

(a) 28   (b) 40   (c) 38   (d) 68

22 The first six square numbers are

$$1, \ 4, \ 9, \ 16, \ 25, \ 36$$

(a) Does this list contain any prime numbers?

(b) From this list write down
    (i) the multiples of 4,   (ii) the multiples of 3.

(c) Write down the next two numbers in the list.

(d) Draw diagrams to show why the numbers in the original list are square numbers.

23 n is a positive whole number and $n > 10$.

(a) Explain why $2n - 1$ is an odd number.

(b) Write down, in terms of n, the next even number after $2n - 1$.

(c) Write down, in terms of n, the next odd number after $2n - 1$.

(d) Find, in terms of n, the sum of the three numbers referred to in parts (a) to (c). Explain why this sum is a multiple of 6.

24 Complete the magic square so that the numbers in each row, column and diagonal add up to 21.

9		
8	7	

25 Complete the magic square so that the numbers in each row, column and diagonal add up to 27.

10		
		5
		8

26 (a) Divide 35 in the ratio $2:3$.

(b) Divide 56 in the ratio $4:3$.

(c) Divide 5.5 in the ratio $9:2$.

(d) Divide 104 in the ratio $11:15$.

(e) Divide 63 in the ratio $2:3:4$.

(f) Divide 432 in the ratio $5:8:11$.

27 If $1440 = 2^x \times 3^y \times 5^z$ find x, y and z.

28 (a) Simplify

(i) $\dfrac{2^2 \times 2^3}{2^4}$ (ii) $\dfrac{3^3 \times 3^4}{3^2}$ (iii) $\dfrac{3^2 \times 3^4}{3^8}$ (iv) $\dfrac{2^4 \times 2^5}{2^3}$

(b) Which is the larger (i) 2^4 or 4^2, (ii) 3^7 or 7^3?

29 Amanda divides £25 by 7 using her calculator. The display shows 3.5714286. What is the answer correct to the nearest penny?

30 (a) My lounge measures 4 m by 3 m, each dimension being correct to the nearest metre. If the exact length is l m and the exact breadth is b m complete the following inequalities.
     (i) $\leqslant l <$ (ii) $\leqslant b <$
  (b) If A m² is the exact area of the room what is
     (i) the smallest possible value for A?
     (ii) the largest possible value for A?

Questions 31 to 37 involve the use of the standard form $a \times 10^n$, where n is an integer and $1 \leqslant a < 10$.

31 The diameter of Mercury is 4960 km. This can be written as 4.96×10^n km. State the value of n.

32 The diameter of Mars is 6750 km. This can be written as $a \times 10^3$ km. State the value of a.

33 The diameter of Jupiter is 89 000 miles. This can be written as 8.9×10^n miles. State the value of n.

34 The distance of the Earth from the Sun is 93 000 000 miles. Write this in the form $a \times 10^n$ miles.

35 The distance of Venus from the Sun is 67 million miles. Express this in the form $a \times 10^n$ miles.

36 The distance of Jupiter from the Sun is 770 000 000 km. Express this in the form $a \times 10^n$ km.

37 The distance of Pluto from the Sun is 5870 million kilometres. Express this in standard form.

38 The distances, in kilometres, of four planets from the Sun are:

Planet	Distance from Sun (km)
A	3.24×10^8
B	6.40×10^7
C	2.24×10^8
D	1.92×10^9

  (a) Which of these planets is nearest the Sun?
  (b) Which of these planets is about 30 times as far from the Sun as planet B?

(c) Find the ratio of the distance of planet B from the Sun to the distance of planet C from the Sun in the form $1:n$.

(d) If light travels at 3×10^5 km/s calculate the time, correct to the nearest minute, that the light from the Sun takes to reach planet D.

39

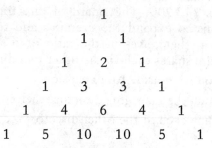

This triangular array of numbers is part of Pascal's triangle.

(a) Write down the next two rows.

(b) Write down the sum of the numbers in each of the first eight rows.

(c) Express each number in (b) in index form.

(d) Write down, in index form, the sum of the numbers
    (i) in the twelfth row,   (ii) in the twenty-first row.

40

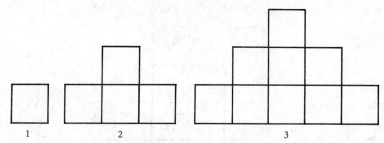

(a) Continue this pattern to give the next two arrangements of square tiles.

(b) Complete the following table which shows the number of tiles required for each design.

Design number	Number of tiles required
1	
2	
3	
4	
5	

(c) How many tiles will be required for
    (i) Design number 8,   (ii) Design number 12?

41 At a football match $\frac{3}{7}$ of the spectators were in the enclosure, $\frac{2}{5}$ were on the terraces and the remaining 5280 were in the stand. Find the total number of spectators at the match.

42 The profit made last year by a small company making printed circuits was £13 200. The board of directors decided to use two-thirds of this to expand the premises and to divide the remaining profit among themselves in the ratio of 5 shares to the managing director and 3 shares each to the other two directors. Calculate

(a) the amount set aside for expansion,

(b) how much the managing director received,

(c) how much each of the other directors received.

43

1	2	3	4	5
6	7	8	9	10
11	12	13	14	15
16	17	18	19	20
21	22	23	24	25
26	27	28	29	30
31	32	33	34	35
36	37	38	39	40

In the rectangular array of numbers shown above the square is called the '27 square' since the number in the top left-hand corner is 27.

(a) What are the numbers in
   (i) the '29 square',   (ii) the '16 square'?

(b) What is the sum of the numbers in
   (i) the '22 square',   (ii) the '36 square'?

(c) Can you write down the numbers in the '25 square'?

(d) What are the numbers in the square if their total is
   (i) 108   (ii) 136?

(e) For the '18 square' find
   (i) the sum of the numbers in each diagonal,
   (ii) the difference between the two sums.

(f) Repeat part (e) for
    (i) the '28 square',   (ii) the '4 square'.
    (iii) What do you think the answer will be for the '26 square'?

(g) What is the answer for the 'n square'?

44   A petrol tank of a car holds 55 litres of petrol when full, and the car consumes petrol at the rate of 1 litre per 15 km. What fraction of the tank still contains petrol after a journey of 165 km if the tank was $\frac{4}{5}$ full before the start of the journey?

45   Each compartment in a railway carriage seats 8 people. There are 6 compartments in a carriage. A school trip to London anticipates that 342 pupils and 21 staff wish to go. How many carriages should a special train have in order to carry this party, assuming that everybody has a seat? How many vacant seats are there?

Sequences   2

1   Write down the next two terms in each of the following sequences.
    (a) 2, 5, 8, 11,   (b) 10, 15, 20, 25,
    (c) 3, 11, 19, 27,   (d) 6, 10, 14, 18,
    (e) −2, −4, −6, −8,   (f) 20, 15, 10, 5,
    (g) 1, 4, 9, 16,   (h) 3, 6, 11, 18,
    (i) $\frac{1}{2}, \frac{2}{3}, \frac{3}{4}, \frac{4}{5},$ (j) 1, 3, 6, 10,
    (k) $1, 1+3, 1+3+5, 1+3+5+7.$

2   Write down an expression for the nth term of each sequence given in question 1, parts (a) to (i).

3   This is a sequence of pairs of numbers.

    $(1, 5), (2, 7), (3, 9), (4, 11), \ldots$

    (a) Write down the next pair in the sequence.
    (b) Find (i) the tenth pair, (ii) the nth pair, in the sequence.

4   Peter is making patterns with squares out of matchsticks.

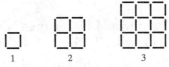

         1   2   3

    (a) How many matchsticks are used to make
        (i) pattern 1, (ii) pattern 2, (iii) pattern 3?
    (b) Without the help of a diagram, find the number of matchsticks required to make
        (i) pattern 4, (ii) pattern 5, (iii) pattern n.

5

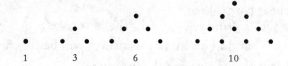

1   3   6   10

These numbers are called triangular numbers.

(a) Write down the next four triangular numbers.

(b) What is the tenth triangular number?

(c) Copy and complete the following table to find the numbers in a new sequence.

1st number = 1st triangular number + 2nd triangular number = 4
2nd number = 3rd triangular number + 4th triangular number = 16
3rd number = 5th triangular number + 6th triangular number =
4th number = 7th triangular number + 8th triangular number =

(d) Write down the next three terms in the new sequence and an expression for the nth term.

6   The first four terms of a sequence are 4, 12, 8, 10, ...

The third term is the mean of the first two, and the fourth term is the mean of the second and third terms. Other terms are found in a similar way.

(a) Write down the fifth and sixth terms in this sequence.

(b) Use the rule given above to form the sequence that starts 12, 4, ... Give the first six terms.

7   In a restaurant chairs can be arranged around the square tables as shown below.

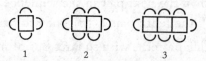

1   2   3

(a) How many chairs would be required when the number of tables arranged in this way is (i) 4, (ii) 5, (iii) 8?

(b) How many chairs would be required when n tables are arranged in this way?

(c) How many tables are needed when 22 chairs are used?

(d) The owner has 37 chairs altogether. Is it possible to arrange tables in this pattern so that all the chairs are used?

8   Sally uses matchsticks to make patterns. One of her patterns is shown below.

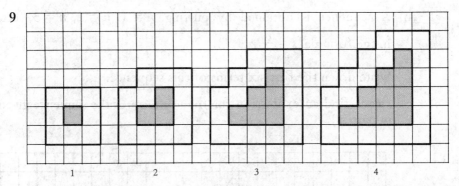

      1   2   3

(a) How many matchsticks does she use to make
    (i) pattern 1,   (ii) pattern 2,   (iii) pattern 3?

(b) How many matchsticks does she need to make
    (i) pattern 10,   (ii) pattern n?

(c) Which pattern does she make if she uses 61 matchsticks?

9

      1   2   3   4

The diagrams show a pattern of black tiles surrounded by white tiles

(a) Draw the next two diagrams in the pattern.

(b) Copy and complete the following table which shows the number of each type of tile needed for the first six diagrams in the pattern.

Diagram number	1	2	3	4	5	6
Number of black tiles	1	3				
Number of white tiles	8	12				

(c) Without drawing a diagram, determine the number of white tiles
    (i) in diagram number 8,
    (ii) when there are 45 black tiles.

(d) Find a rule which gives the number of white tiles, w, and the number of black tiles, b, for the nth diagram in the pattern.

(e) Use the rule you established in part (d) to find
    (i) the number of black tiles when there are 52 white tiles,
    (ii) the number of white tiles when there are 55 black tiles.

(f) Is there any value of n for which there are equal numbers of black and white tiles?

10 The first three terms of a sequence are 2, 3, 5, ...

(a) If these numbers are the first three terms of the sequence of prime numbers, write down the next six terms.

(b) If other numbers in the sequence do not have to be prime numbers write down another way of continuing the sequence. State the rule you are using.

11 (a) The first six terms of a sequence are

2, 6, 12, 20, 30, 42, ...

(i) Write down the next two terms.
(ii) Explain why all the numbers in this sequence are even.

(b) A sequence is obtained by putting $n = 1$, $n = 2$, $n = 3$, etc. in the formula $s = \dfrac{n}{2}(n + 1)$.

Write down the first six terms of this sequence.

Hence find an expression for the nth term of the sequence given in part (a).

12

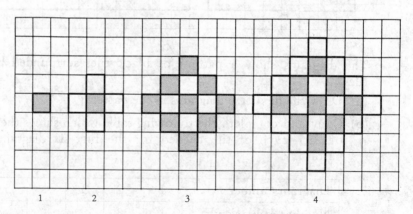

(a) Study the tiling pattern given above, then copy and complete the following table.

Pattern number	1	2	3	4
Number of black tiles	1	1		
Number of white tiles	0	4		
Total number of tiles	1	5		

(b) Without drawing pattern number 5 add column 5 to the table and go on to add column 6.

(c) Is it true to say that the total number of tiles used is equal to the sum of the squares of two consecutive whole numbers?

(d) Which two consecutive whole numbers need to be squared to give the total number of tiles used
    (i) in pattern number 7,
    (ii) in pattern number 10?

(e) Show that the total number of tiles used in pattern number n is $2n^2 - 2n + 1$.

(f) Which pattern number uses 265 tiles?

Basic Algebra   3

Simplify where possible.

1 (a) $5x + 2x$ (b) $2x - 2$
    (c) $4a + b - 2a$ (d) $5a^2 + a$
    (e) $3x^2 + 2x^2 - 4x^2$ (f) $a + 3b - 2a$

2 (a) $4a - a - 3a$ (b) $7x - 9x$
    (c) $x^2 + x$ (d) $3a - 7a$
    (e) $x + 5x - 3x$ (f) $12a - 3a - 5a$

3 (a) $8a - (-3a)$ (b) $4a - (-7a) + a$
    (c) $b^2 - (-b)$ (d) $5b - b + (-3b)$

4 (a) $3x^2 - 5x + 4x - 2$ (b) $7a^2 + 9a - 3a + 2$
    (c) $x^2 + 6x - 6x + 36$ (d) $4b^2 - 5a + 2a - 5$

5 (a) $2a \times 3a$ (b) $5a \times b$
    (c) $3x \times 4x$ (d) $3a \times (-2a)$
    (e) $4x \times (-2x)$ (f) $(-5x) \times (2x)$

Remove the brackets and simplify.

6 (a) $5(2x + 3)$ (b) $4(5a - 2)$
    (c) $3(5x - 2)$ (d) $7(3 + 2a)$
    (e) $4(5 - 3a)$ (f) $5a(a + 3)$

7 (a) $4(x + 3) + 3(x + 1)$ (b) $5(a + 4) + 2(a + 1)$
    (c) $3(x + 5) + 3(x + 7)$ (d) $2(a + 2) + 3(2a + 5)$

8 (a) $5(a + 4) - 2(a + 2)$ (b) $8(2x - 1) - 5(x + 1)$
    (c) $3(x - 2) - 2(x - 7)$ (d) $3(a + 5) - 4(a - 3)$

9 (a) $x(x + 7) + 3x$ (b) $5a - a(a + 1)$
    (c) $x(x + 3) - 5$ (d) $x(2x + 7) - 5x$
    (e) $2a(a - 4) - 5a$ (f) $4x(x + 3) - 3x - 4x$

10 (a) $x(x + 3) + x(x - 2)$ (b) $2a(a + 4) - a(a + 5)$
    (c) $5x(x - 3) - 2x(x + 3)$ (d) $4a(a - 5) - 3a(a - 4)$

Expand and simplify.

11 (a) $(x + 2)(x + 3)$ (b) $(x + 4)(x + 7)$
    (c) $(x + 5)(x + 1)$ (d) $(x + 2)(x + 6)$

12 (a) $(x - 4)(x - 3)$ (b) $(x - 5)(x - 6)$
    (c) $(x - 3)(x - 10)$ (d) $(x - 1)(x - 9)$

13 (a) $(x + 7)(x - 3)$ (b) $(x + 9)(x - 4)$
    (c) $(x - 3)(x + 5)$ (d) $(x - 10)(x + 7)$

14 (a) $(a + 4)(a - 4)$ (b) $(x - 7)(x + 7)$
    (c) $(a + 5)^2$ (d) $(x - 4)^2$

Factorise.

15 (a) $4x + 8$ (b) $9a + 6$
    (c) $5t + 10$ (d) $3a - 6$
    (e) $10 - 5a$ (f) $12x - 16$

16 (a) $x^2 + 7x$ (b) $x^2 + 12x$
    (c) $3a^2 + 3$ (d) $5a^2 - a$
    (e) $4a^2 - 2a$ (f) $6x^2 - 12x$

Solve the following equations.

17 (a) $x + 4 = 9$ (b) $x + 7 = 10$
    (c) $x + 3 = 7$ (d) $x - 5 = 10$
    (e) $x - 3 = 9$ (f) $x - 1 = 14$

18 (a) $3x + 1 = 10$ (b) $4x + 3 = 15$
    (c) $2x + 8 = 18$ (d) $5x - 2 = 13$
    (e) $3x - 5 = 19$ (f) $6x - 12 = 0$

19 (a) $5(x - 2) = 10$ (b) $3(x + 4) = 21$
    (c) $2(2x - 7) = 8$ (d) $2(x + 1) = 7$
    (e) $3(x - 4) = 1$ (f) $5(2x - 1) = 13$

20 (a) $5(x - 6) = 3(x - 4)$ (b) $4(5x - 8) = 7(x + 1)$
    (c) $5(3x + 4) = 2(3x + 1)$ (d) $6(3x + 2) = 7(x - 3)$
    (e) $11(2x + 3) = 7(2x - 1)$ (f) $2(x - 8) = 3(x - 9)$
    (g) $3(x + 7) = 7(3 - x)$ (h) $3(8x + 7) = 5(2x + 7)$

21 (a) $\dfrac{x}{2} = 3$ (b) $\dfrac{x}{3} = 5$

    (c) $\dfrac{x}{5} = 2$ (d) $\dfrac{x}{4} = -2$

    (e) $\dfrac{x}{5} = -3$ (f) $\dfrac{x}{8} = \dfrac{3}{4}$

22 (a) $\dfrac{x+1}{2} = 1$ (b) $\dfrac{x-3}{5} = 2$

    (c) $\dfrac{2x+1}{3} = 5$ (d) $\dfrac{3x-1}{5} = 4$

23 (a) $5 - \dfrac{x}{2} = 1$ (b) $2 + \dfrac{x}{3} = \dfrac{1}{2}$

    (c) $7 + \dfrac{3x}{4} = 19$ (d) $\dfrac{x+7}{4} - 3 = 0$

24 (a) $x + \dfrac{1}{4} = \dfrac{1}{2}$ (b) $x - \dfrac{1}{3} = \dfrac{1}{6}$

    (c) $x - \dfrac{2}{5} = \dfrac{3}{10}$ (d) $x + \dfrac{2}{5} = \dfrac{3}{5}$

25 (a) $\dfrac{x+1}{3} = \dfrac{x-3}{4}$ (b) $\dfrac{x+12}{7} = \dfrac{x-4}{3}$

26 (a) $\dfrac{3x-2}{4} = \dfrac{2x+8}{5}$ (b) $\dfrac{5x-1}{7} = \dfrac{3x-1}{4}$

27 Complete each of these.
    (a) $(x + 4)(x + 5) = x^2 \qquad + 20$
    (b) $(a + 3)(a + 7) = a^2 + 10a$
    (c) $(x - 4)(x - 6) = x^2 - 10x$
    (d) $(b - 2)(b - 5) = b^2 \qquad + 10$
    (e) $(x + 3)(x - 7) = x^2 - 4x$
    (f) $(x - 5)(x + 6) = x^2 \qquad - 30$
    (g) $(5 - c)(8 - c) = 40$
    (h) $(y - 4)(y - 3) = y^2 - 7y$

28 Remove the brackets and simplify.
    (a) $(x + 6)(2x + 1)$ (b) $(x + 3)(3x + 3)$
    (c) $(4x + 7)(x - 5)$ (d) $(5x + 2)(x - 4)$
    (e) $(x + 6)(7x - 5)$ (f) $(x - 3)(3x + 6)$
    (g) $(4x - 3)(x - 6)$ (h) $(9x - 7)(x - 4)$

29 Remove the brackets and simplify.

(a) $(4x + 7)(3x + 2)$
(b) $(7x + 5)(6x + 3)$
(c) $(8x - 5)(3x - 7)$
(d) $(10x - 1)(2x - 3)$
(e) $(5x - 4)(2x + 1)$
(f) $(6x + 2)(3x - 1)$
(g) $(4x + 3)(4x - 3)$
(h) $(5x - 4)(5x + 2)$

Simultaneous Linear Equations 4

Solve the given pairs of simultaneous linear equations.

1 $x + y = 5$
   $x - y = 1$

2 $x + y = 7$
   $x - y = 3$

3 $3x + y = 13$
   $2x - y = 2$

4 $4x + y = 14$
   $2x + y = 8$

5 $4x - y = 14$
   $5x - y = 17$

6 $3x + y = 11$
   $5x + y = 19$

7 $3x + 2y = 17$
   $x - y = 4$

8 $4x + 3y = 5$
   $5x - y = 11$

9 $4x - y = 8$
   $3x - 2y = 11$

10 $5x + 3y = 29$
    $4x - y = 13$

11 $4x + 3y = 0$
    $x + y = 1$

12 $7x - y = 12$
    $3x - 2y = 2$

13 A year ago David's father was four times as old as David. In two years' time he will be three times as old as David. How old is David?

14 A pen and a pencil cost 24 p. If two pens and three pencils cost 56 p find the cost of

(a) a pen,

(b) a pencil,

(c) three pens and two pencils.

15 The sum of Peter's age and his father's age is 40 years. In two years time Peter's father will be three times as old as Peter. Let p and f represent their ages in years and write two equations connecting p and f. Solve these equations to find the present age of each.

16 Philip pays £1.20 for three pens and two pencils, while Sandra pays £1.95 for four pens and five pencils. Without finding the cost of each, find the cost of two pens and two pencils.

17 Two numbers are such that if 14 is added to the first the answer is three times the second, while if 6 is subtracted from the first the answer is half the second. Find the two numbers.

18 In a supermarket 3 jars of lime marmalade together with 5 jars of orange marmalade cost £4.30, while 5 jars of lime and 4 jars of orange cost £5. Find the cost of each type of marmalade per jar.

19 A housewife buys 4 jars of coffee and 3 packets of tea for £9.40 while a second housewife buys 5 jars of coffee and 6 packets of tea for £13.55. If a third housewife buys one jar of each how much will she have to pay?

20 It costs £1.18 to send three letters by first-class post and two letters by second–class post. If it costs £1.50 to send five letters first class and one letter second class find the cost of sending
  (a) one first-class letter,   (b) one second-class letter.

Formulas   5

1 Find the value of each of the following expressions when $a = 3$, $b = 4$ and $c = 6$.
  (a) $a + b + c$ (b) $ab + c$
  (c) abc (d) $3a + 4b$
  (e) $3b - 2c$ (f) $5a + b - 2c$
  (g) $a^2 + b^2$ (h) $\sqrt{a^2 + b^2}$
  (i) $\sqrt{\frac{1}{2}abc}$ (j) $\dfrac{1}{a} + \dfrac{1}{c}$
  (k) $\dfrac{ab}{c}$ (l) $c^2 - b^2 - a^2$

2 If $A = lb$ find
  (a) A when $l = 4$ and $b = 5$,
  (b) l when $A = 28$ and $b = 4$,
  (c) b when $A = 48$ and $l = 16$.

3 If $A = \frac{1}{2}bh$ find
  (a) A when $b = 7$ and $h = 6$,
  (b) h when $A = 14$ and $b = 7$,
  (c) b when $h = 8$ and $A = 36$.

4 If $p = 2(a + b)$ find
  (a) p when $a = 5$ and $b = 7$,
  (b) b when $a = 11$ and $p = 40$.

17

5 The cost, £C, of hiring a concrete mixer is given by the formula $C = 4 + 5n$ where n is the number of days for which it is hired. Find the cost of hiring the mixer for

(a) 2 days,   (b) 6 days,   (c) one week.

6 The quarterly telephone bill, C pence, is given by the formula $C = 1500 + 5x$ where x is the number of units used.

(a) What is the standing charge, i.e. the amount that must be paid whether or not any units are consumed?

(b) Find the cost in £s when the number of units used is
(i) 100,   (ii) 3500.

7 The cost, £C, of taking a group of pupils on an outing is given by the formula $C = 50 + 3n$ where n is the number of pupils.

(a) Find the cost of taking 48 pupils on the outing.

(b) How many pupils go if the total cost is £182?

8 The cost, £C, of running a car for a year is given by the formula $C = 500 + \dfrac{px}{50}$ where x is the number of miles travelled and p is the cost in £s of one gallon of petrol.

(a) Find the cost when $p = 2$ and $x = 10\,000$.

(b) Find the distance travelled when $C = 740$ and $p = 1.5$.

9 The number of teachers, N, in a school is given by the formula $N = \dfrac{x}{16} + \dfrac{y}{12}$ where x is the number of pupils in years 1 to 5, and y is the number of pupils in the sixth form. A school has 720 pupils in years 1 to 5 and 180 in the sixth form.

(a) Write down the value of (i) x, (ii) y.

(b) How many teachers are there?

10 The highest of three consecutive whole numbers is n. If the sum of the three numbers is s find a formula connecting s and n.

11 The lowest of three consecutive even numbers is n. If the sum of the three numbers is s find a formula connecting s and n.

12 The middle number of three consecutive positive odd numbers is n. If the sum of the three numbers is s find a formula connecting s and n.

13 The highest of three consecutive whole numbers is n. If this number is subtracted from the sum of the other two the answer is D.
  (a) Find a formula connecting n and D.
  (b) Find (i) D if $n = 7$,   (ii) n if $D = 12$.

14 Tickets for a concert cost £8 for adults and £5 for children.
  (a) How much will the tickets cost for
    (i) 3 adults,   (ii) 10 adults,   (iii) p adults?
  (b) How much will it cost for tickets for
    (i) 4 children,   (ii) 15 children,   (iii) q children?
  (c) If £C is the total cost for p adults and q children find a formula for C in terms of p and q.

15 Petrol costs 50p per litre and oil costs £1.50 per litre.
  (a) How much will it cost, in pounds, for
    (i) 2,   (ii) 5,   (iii) x, litres of petrol?
  (b) How much will it cost, in pounds, for
    (i) 4,   (ii) 7,   (iii) y, litres of oil?
  (c) Make a formula for the total cost, £C, of x litres of petrol and y litres of oil.

16 Make the letter in brackets the subject of the formula.
  (a) $a = b + c$ (b)
  (b) $A = bh$ (b)
  (c) $y = mx + c$ (c)
  (d) $C = 2\pi R$ (R)
  (e) $C = \pi D$ (π)
  (f) $p = \dfrac{12}{v}$ (v)
  (g) $v = abc$ (b)
  (h) $v = \frac{1}{3}\pi r^2 h$ (h)
  (i) $v = \frac{4}{3}\pi r^3$ (π)
  (j) $y = ax - b$ (b)

17 The area of a trapezium with parallel sides of lengths a and b is given by the formula $A = \frac{1}{2}(a + b)h$ where h is the perpendicular distance between the parallel sides.

(a) Find h if $A = 40\,\text{cm}^2$ when $a = 7\,\text{cm}$ and $b = 9\,\text{cm}$.

(b) Find a if $A = 80\,\text{cm}^2$ when $b = 12\,\text{cm}$ and $h = 8\,\text{cm}$.

18 The volume of a pyramid is given by the formula $V = \frac{1}{3}Ah$ where A is the area of the base and h is the perpendicular height.

(a) Find h if $V = 20\,\text{cm}^3$ when $A = 12\,\text{cm}^2$.

(b) Find A if $V = 32\,\text{cm}^3$ when $h = 12\,\text{cm}$.

19 An approximate relationship between a temperature measured as °F (Fahrenheit) or °C (Celsius) is

'To find F, add 15 to C and double your answer.'

(a) Write this as a formula.

(b) Hence estimate F when $C = -30$.

(c) What is the equivalent rule to find C when F is given?

(d) If $F = \frac{9}{5}C + 32$ find the exact value of F when $C = -30$.

(e) The classroom temperature is 16 °C, correct to the nearest degree. What is the range of possible values of this temperature in °F?

Percentages

6

1 Convert each of the following decimals into a percentage.

(a) 0.5 (b) 0.8

(c) 0.75 (d) 0.35

(e) 0.68 (f) 2.25

(g) 0.26 (h) 1.74

2 Convert each of the following percentages into a common fraction in its lowest terms.

(a) 30% (b) 60%

(c) 25% (d) 45%

(e) 150% (f) 175%

(g) $67\frac{1}{2}\%$ (h) $33\frac{1}{3}\%$

3 Express the first quantity as a percentage of the second.

(a) 50p, £1 (b) 40 cm, 1 m

(c) 64p, £2 (d) 8 hours, 1 day

(e) 15 km, 120 km (f) 24 cm, 600 mm

4   Find
   (a) 20% of £1   (b) 30% of 8 metres
   (c) 75% of 8 litres   (d) 120% of £5
   (e) $12\frac{1}{2}$% of £7.20   (f) $66\frac{2}{3}$% of 63 kg.

5   In a sale, marked prices are reduced by 10%.
   (a) How much would George have to pay for a soccer ball marked
        £22?
   (b) Shirley paid £81 for a winter coat. What was the marked price?

6   A calculator is advertised at £10.20 with a discount of 20% for cash.
   What is the cash price?

7   A builders' merchant allows a discount of $2\frac{1}{2}$% for cash sales. What
   would be the cash price of an article marked £16?

8   A joint of meat loses 8% of its weight when thawed. If a piece of
   beef weighs 1.5 kg when taken from the freezer, what does it weigh
   when thawed out?

9   In Horton Comprehensive School 64% of the pupils study German
   and 648 do not. How many pupils are there in the school?

10 A retailer buys 30 boxes of strawberries at 35p each and sells 27 of
   them at 30% profit, the other three boxes being thrown away. How
   much profit did he make?

11 A couple decide to buy a house costing £75 200. A building society is
   prepared to advance 90% of the purchase price. The monthly repayments are at the rate of 90p per £100 (or part £100) borrowed,
   over a period of 20 years. Calculate
   (a) the amount borrowed,
   (b) the yearly repayment to the building society,
   (c) the total cost of the house.

12 A retailer bought 52 cassettes at £5.25 each. He broke two and sold
   the rest at 30% profit. Find his total profit.

13 A video recorder cost £385 in a sale when a discount of 30% is given.
   What was the original selling price?

21

14 Find the cash price of each of the following items when the rate of value added tax (VAT) is $17\frac{1}{2}\%$.

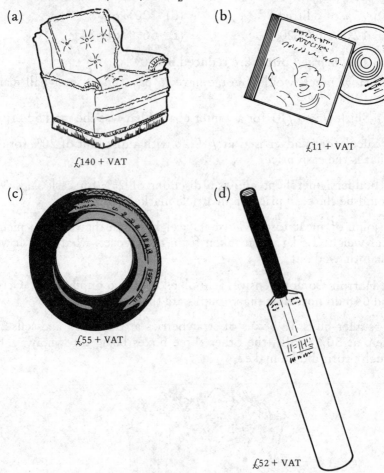

(a)

£140 + VAT

(b)

£11 + VAT

(c)

£55 + VAT

(d)

£52 + VAT

15 Find the cash price of each of the following items when the rate of VAT is 20%.

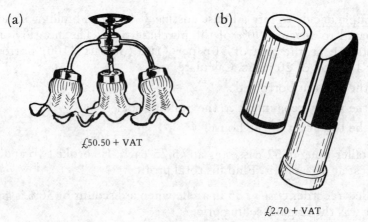

(a)

£50.50 + VAT

(b)

£2.70 + VAT

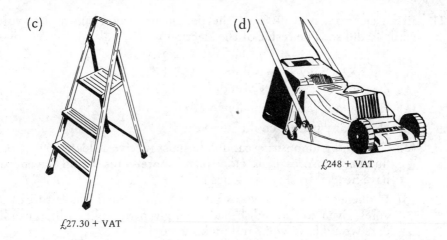

(c)

(d)

£248 + VAT

£27.30 + VAT

16 A housewife bought several articles which were priced exclusive of VAT at $17\frac{1}{2}\%$; a bucket at 60p, a pair of steps at £14.58, a dustbin at £7.20 and a clothes line at £13.12. Calculate the total bill including the value added tax.

17 A businessman is charged £248.16 for four tyres for his van, the cost including value added tax at $17\frac{1}{2}\%$. Since he is in business he claims repayment of the VAT. How much does each tyre actually cost him?

18 An electric typewriter costs £500.55 including value added tax at $17\frac{1}{2}\%$. A businessman finds that the VAT is refunded at a later date, whereas the private customer must pay the full price. Calculate the difference between the two prices.

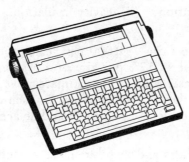

19 A motor scooter is priced at £800 plus VAT at $17\frac{1}{2}\%$.
(a) Find the total price including VAT.
(b) Speedstore offers a discount of 10% off the total price while Motorama offers a cash discount of £65 off the marked price. Which dealer gives the better deal, and by how much?

20 Ellaways offer a compact disc player at £150 plus VAT at $17\frac{1}{2}\%$. Denham's offer the same unit at £176 including VAT. Which store offers the better deal, and by how much?

21 In an election, only 70% of the people who were allowed to vote actually did so. The result of the election was

Aplin   14 286
Bolter   17 176
Cavendish   3 755

(a) How many people actually voted?

(b) How many people could have voted?

(c) To save his deposit, a candidate must receive at least 15% of the number of votes cast. How many more votes would Cavendish have needed to save his deposit?

(d) If one-eighth of the votes given to Bolter and one-fifth of the votes given to Cavendish had been given to Aplin, which candidate would have won, and by how much?

22 The Davis family spend £1200 each year on heating their home. They consider three ways of cutting their fuel bills.

	Cost of installation	Reduction in annual heating cost
Loft insulation	£360	20%
Cavity insulation	£900	25%
Double glazing	£4800	10%

(a) Calculate the amount saved annually in each case.

(b) How many years will it take before the saving covers the installation costs for
(i) loft insulation,   (ii) cavity insulation,   (iii) double glazing?

23 Franz Bloch, who earns £18 000 per year, negotiates for a pay rise. He is offered either a 12% pay rise or a 5% pay rise plus a company car with all expenses paid. Franz estimates that his own car costs him 33p per mile for the 8000 miles he covers each year. Find the increase he will receive in each case. Which should he accept?

24 A family of 2 adults and 2 children select a suitable summer holiday from a travel brochure. The brochure price is £612 per person. Each child is given a 15% discount on the brochure price. In addition they must pay airport taxes which amount to £22.50 per person and insurance which is £26.10 per person. The brochure states that the price may be subject to a surcharge, but that this will not be more than 10% of the brochure price. Find the maximum amount which the family could be asked to pay for their holiday. If there are no surcharges find

(a) the total cost of the holiday,

(b) the average cost per person.

25 The table given below shows the prices of tickets for a festival. Discounts are given to those who attend more than two concerts, e.g. a person who buys tickets for five concerts receives a 20% discount.

	Price Range			
Season Tickets	£11	£15	£19	
Six concerts (25%)	£49.50	£67.50	£85.50	£99
Five concerts (20%)		£60.00	£76.00	
Four concerts (15%)	£37.40	£51.00	£64.60	£74.80
Three concerts (10%)		£40.50	£51.30	£59.40

Use the information given in the table to find

(a) the total cost, without discount, for one person to attend five concerts at the lowest price,

(b) the cost of a five-concert season ticket for seats costing £15.00 each,

(c) the cost of a five-concert season ticket for seats costing £11.00 each,

(d) the cost of the most expensive seat,

(e) the lowest total cost for two people to attend six concerts. How much is saved by buying a season ticket?

(f) the cost of two season tickets for three concerts for the cheapest seats.

Parallel Lines, Triangles and Quadrilaterals 7

In each diagram find the angles marked with letters.

1

2

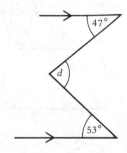

3

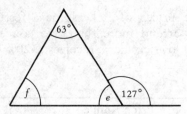

4

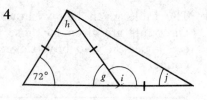

5

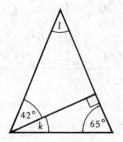

6

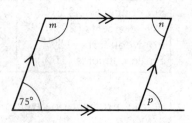

7

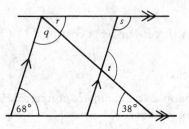

8

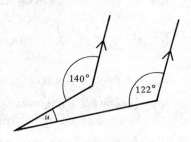

9

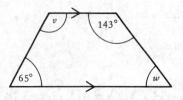

10

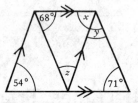

11

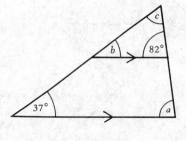

12

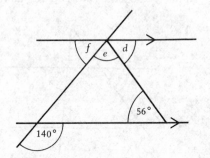

13

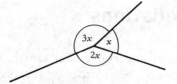

14

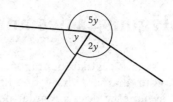

15

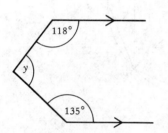

16

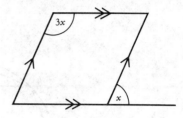

17

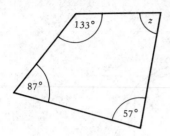

18

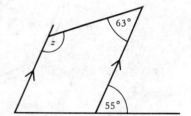

19

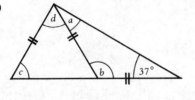

20

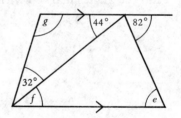

21

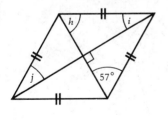

22

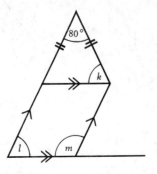

Polygons, Tiles and Tessellations 8

1 Draw a regular pentagon with a side of any convenient length. On your diagram draw one line of symmetry. What order of rotational symmetry does a regular pentagon possess?

2

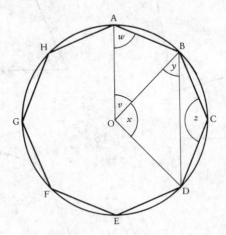

The diagram shows a regular octagon inscribed in a circle centre O. Find the angles marked with the letters v, w, x, y and z.

3

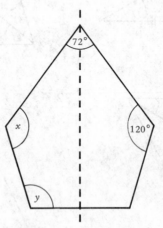

The diagram shows a pentagon which has just one axis of symmetry. Find the angles marked x and y.

4

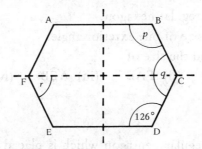

The hexagon ABCDEF has just two axes of symmetry. Find the angles marked *p, q* and *r*.

5 A regular polygon has 10 sides. What is the size of
   (a) an exterior angle,   (b) an interior angle?

6 A regular polygon has 15 sides. What is the size of
   (a) an exterior angle,   (b) an interior angle?

7 The exterior angle of a regular polygon is 30°.
   (a) What is the size of an interior angle?
   (b) How many sides does the polygon have?

8 The interior angle of a regular polygon is 160°.
   (a) What is the size of an exterior angle?
   (b) How many sides does the polygon have?

9 Is it possible to have a regular polygon with an exterior angle of
   (a) 30°   (b) 40°
   (c) 50°   (d) 60°?

10 Is it possible to have a regular polygon with an interior angle of
   (a) 120°   (b) 130°
   (c) 140°   (d) 145°?

11 A pentagon has angles $x°$, $(x-5)°$, $(x+10)°$, $(x+20)°$ and $(x+15)°$. Find x.

12 The angles of a hexagon are, in order, $x°, x°, (x-20)°, x°, x°$ and $(x-10)°$. Find x. Are any of the sides parallel?

13

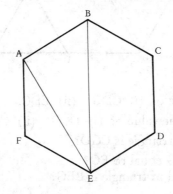

ABCDEF is a regular hexagon.

(a) Find the size of one exterior angle.

(b) Hence find the size of

    (i) A$\hat{\text{F}}$E   (ii) F$\hat{\text{A}}$E   (iii) A$\hat{\text{E}}$B   (iv) B$\hat{\text{A}}$E   (v) B$\hat{\text{E}}$D.

14 ABCDE is a regular pentagon which is placed so that DC is horizontal.

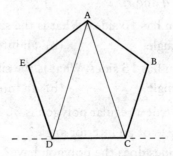

Find

(a) the angle between ED and the horizontal,

(b) (i) A$\hat{\text{E}}$D   (ii) E$\hat{\text{D}}$A   (iii) A$\hat{\text{D}}$C   (iv) D$\hat{\text{A}}$C.

15 ABCDEF is a regular hexagon. The sides BC and ED are produced to meet at G.

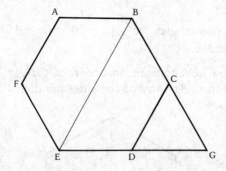

(a) Find the value of (i) C$\hat{\text{D}}$G   (ii) E$\hat{\text{D}}$C.

(b) Write down the value of (i) D$\hat{\text{C}}$G   (ii) C$\hat{\text{G}}$D.

(c) What kind of triangle is CGD?

(d) (i) Why is BG equal to EG?

    (ii) What kind of triangle is BEG?

16

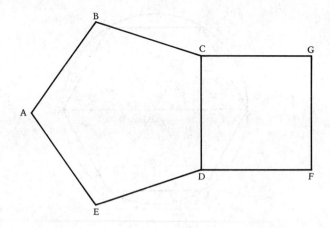

ABCDE is a regular pentagon and CDFG is a square. Find

(a) GĈD   (b) BĈD   (c) BĈG.

17

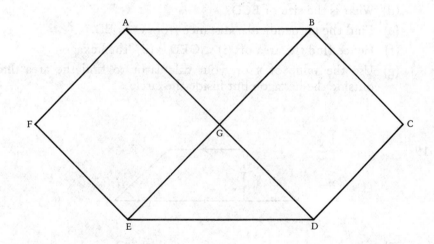

In the hexagon ABCDEF, the diagonals intersect at G. AGEF and BCDG are squares of side 10 cm.

(a) Write down the size of each of the angles of the hexagon.

(b) How many axes of symmetry does the hexagon have?

(c) Calculate the total area of the hexagon.

(d) Calculate the perimeter of the hexagon giving your answer correct to 3 s.f.

(e) If the hexagon is rotated about G through 180° find the new position of (i) A   (ii) E.

18

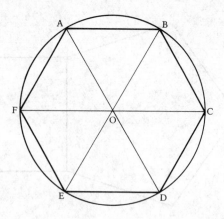

ABCDEF is a regular hexagon inscribed in a circle, centre O, which has a radius of 5 cm.

(a) How many axes of symmetry are there?

(b) What is the size of $A\widehat{O}B$?

(c) What special name is given to triangle AOB?

(d) What is the size of $B\widehat{C}D$?

(e) Find the perpendicular distance from O to ED.

(f) Hence find the area of (i) $\triangle$OED (ii) the hexagon.

(g) Use the value of π on your calculator to find the area that is outside the hexagon but inside the circle.

19

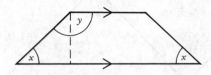

The diagram shows the top of a table that is used in the domestic science room.

(a) What name do we give to this shape? How many lines of symmetry does it have?

(b) If $x = 45°$ write down the value of y.

(c) Show how two of these tables can be put together to form a hexagon. Is this a regular hexagon?

(d) If $x = 45°$ show how four such tables can be arranged to form a square. What is the area of the square gap in the centre of this arrangement, if the shorter of the parallel sides of each table is of length 50 cm?

(e) What is the relationship between x and y if the hexagon formed by two tables is regular?

20 The diagram shows the position of the twelve numbers on the face of a clock, together with the centre, O.

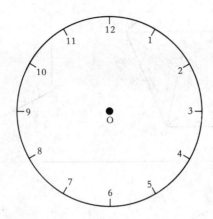

(a) What angle does the hour hand turn through between 1 p.m. and 4 p.m.?

(b) What angle does the minute hand turn through in
(i) 1 hour, (ii) 5 minutes?

(c) Join, in order, the positions of the hours which are multiples of 3, to give a quadrilateral. What name is given to this shape?

(d) Repeat part (c) for the first two and last two odd numbers.

(e) Join, in order, the four odd prime numbers on the face, to give a quadrilateral. Does this quadrilateral contain any right angles?

21 (a) Draw all the possible diagonals for each of the polygons given below. The first three have been completed for you. Then complete the table.

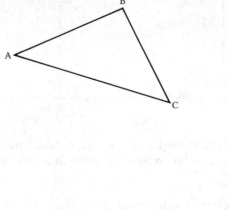

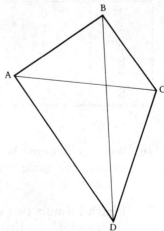

33

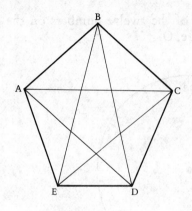 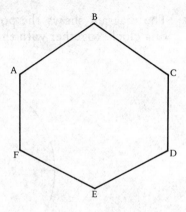

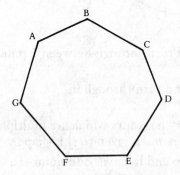 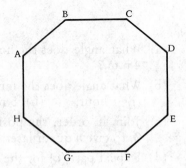

Number of sides (n)	Number of diagonals that can be drawn from A (d)	Number of new diagonals that can be drawn from B C D E F G H	Total number of diagonals (D)
3	0		
4	1	1	
5	2	2 1	
6			
7			
8			

(b) Without drawing polygons, write down the entries that would extend the table for a polygon with 9 sides and one with 10 sides.

(c) Find a formula that gives D in terms of
   (i) n and d,   (ii) n.

34

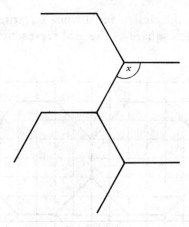

The diagram shows a small section of a patio which is covered completely with identical paving stones, each in the form of a regular polygon. Calculate the value of x. How many sides does each paving stone have? Draw the pattern for eight adjacent stones.

23 The diagram shows part of a floor design using two shapes of tile. The large tiles are regular polygons.

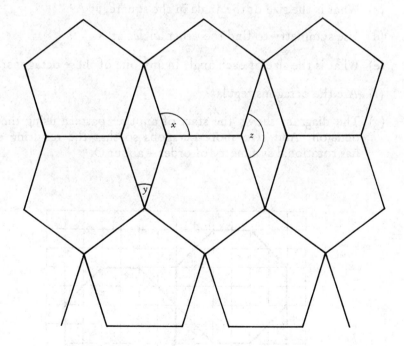

   (a) What name is given to the shape of each of the large tiles?
   (b) What name is given to the shape of each of the small tiles?
   (c) Calculate the value of (i) x (ii) y (iii) z.

24 Given below is the design for a floor covering made up of octagons and squares. Each square of the grid represents 1 cm.

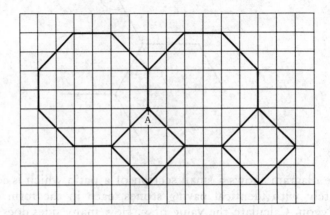

(a) Copy and continue the design by adding two more octagons and two more squares.

(b) Find the area of (i) a square, (ii) an octagon.

(c) What is the size of the angle in the square, at A?

(d) Use symmetry to find the other angles at A.

(e) What is the size of each angle in any one of these octagons?

(f) Are the octagons regular?

(g) The diagram shows the start of another pattern using the same octagon. Add two more octagons so that the resulting design has rotational symmetry of order 4 about O.

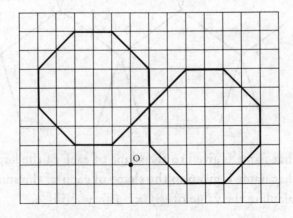

25   The diagram shows the pattern on a square floor tile of side 6 inches, which is coloured in red (the shaded area) and yellow.

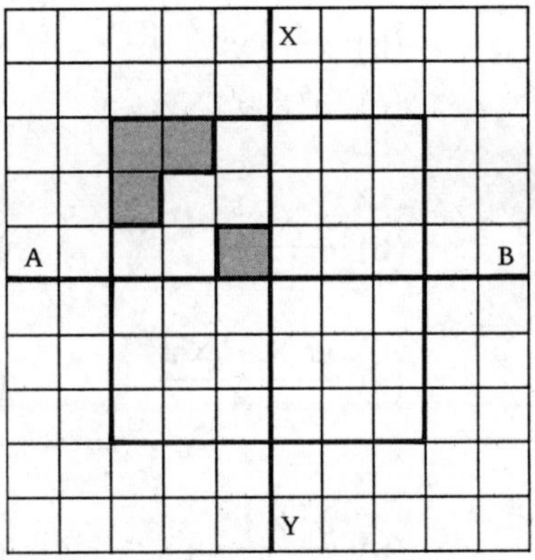

The tiles are laid in fours so that the resulting pattern is symmetrical about both XY and AB.

(a) Draw, on squared paper, the pattern for four tiles.

(b) What fraction of one tile is coloured (i) red,   (ii) yellow?

(c) What fraction of the pattern for four tiles is coloured yellow?

(d) The tiles are to be laid, in fours, to cover a rectangular area measuring 12 feet by 8 feet. They can be bought in complete boxes, each box containing just enough tiles to cover $1\frac{1}{2}$ square yards, and costing £16.20 per box.
   (i) How many tiles are required?
  (ii) How many tiles are there in one box?
 (iii) How many boxes must be bought to have enough to complete the job?
  (iv) How much does it cost to buy the tiles?
   (v) How many tiles are left over?
   [1 yard = 3 feet, 1 foot = 12 inches.]

Indices   9

Simplify each of these.

1   (a) $a^2 \times a^5$ (b) $a^7 \times a^4$
     (c) $x^2 \times x^3$ (d) $x^{12} \times x^7$
     (e) $a^5 \times a$ (f) $x^2 \times x^3 \times x^4$

2 (a) $a^5 \div a^2$ (b) $x^4 \div x^3$ (c) $b^6 \div b^5$
   (d) $t^4 \div t$ (e) $a^7 \div a^7$ (f) $x^7 \div x^3$

3 (a) $x^2 \div x^4$ (b) $x^5 \div x^8$ (c) $a \div a^3$
   (d) $b^2 \div b^3$ (e) $a^5 \div a^6$ (f) $c^3 \div c^3$

4 (a) $\dfrac{a^3 \times a^2}{a^4}$ (b) $\dfrac{x \times x^5}{x^2}$ (c) $\dfrac{b^2 \times b}{b^3}$

   (d) $\dfrac{a \times a^3}{a^2}$ (e) $\dfrac{a^2 \times a^3 \times a}{a^4}$ (f) $\dfrac{b^3 \times b^4 \times b^2}{b^5}$

5 (a) $\dfrac{a^2 \times a^5}{a^8}$ (b) $\dfrac{b^7 \times b^3}{b^{12}}$ (c) $\dfrac{x^2 \times x^4}{x^7}$

   (d) $\dfrac{x \times x^2 \times x^3}{x^7}$ (e) $\dfrac{a^4 \times a^3}{a^7}$ (f) $\dfrac{a^3 \times a^4}{a^{12}}$

6 (a) $2a^2 \times 3a^3$ (b) $3x^3 \times 2x^4$ (c) $5b^3 \times 2b$
   (d) $4a^3 \times 3a^3$ (e) $6x \times 3x^4$ (f) $5x^2 \times 3x^5$

7 (a) $2a^2b \times 3b^2$ (b) $4a^3b \times 2ab^3$ (c) $8ab^2 \times 2a^2$
   (d) $6a^2b^2 \times a^2b$ (e) $5ab \times ab^2$ (f) $3ab^2 \times 2ab^2$

8 (a) $4a \div 2a$ (b) $6a \div 3a$ (c) $24a^2 \div 12a$
   (d) $16b^2 \div 4b$ (e) $25a^3 \div 5a^2$ (f) $18a^3 \div 9a$

9 (a) $12a^2b \div 3ab$ (b) $6ab^2 \div 2ab$
   (c) $15a^4b^2 \div 5a^3b$ (d) $18ab^2 \div 9ab$
   (e) $12a^4b^2 \div 4a^2b$ (f) $27a^5b^3 \div 9a^3b$

Find the value of.

10 (a) 2^3 (b) 3^3 (c) $(\frac{1}{2})^2$ (d) $(\frac{2}{3})^2$
    (e) 2^5 (f) 3^4 (g) 1^3 (h) $(\frac{3}{2})^2$

11 (a) 2^{-1} (b) 3^{-2} (c) 4^{-1} (d) 2^{-2}
    (e) 3^{-3} (f) 5^{-2} (g) 7^0 (h) 7^{-1}

12 (a) $4^{\frac{1}{2}}$ (b) $9^{\frac{1}{2}}$ (c) $16^{\frac{1}{2}}$ (d) $36^{\frac{1}{2}}$
    (e) $(\frac{25}{4})^{\frac{1}{2}}$ (f) $(\frac{9}{49})^{\frac{1}{2}}$ (g) $(\frac{4}{9})^{\frac{1}{2}}$ (h) $(\frac{25}{9})^{\frac{1}{2}}$

Scale Drawings and Loci

1   The scale of the plan of a house is $1:100$.
    (a) What length, in metres, does 1 cm on the plan represent?
    (b) What will be the dimensions of a room which is shown on the plan by a rectangle measuring 4 cm by 3 cm?
    (c) A rectangular bedroom measures 3 m by 2.5 m. On the plan
        (i) what are the measurements of this room,
        (ii) what is its area?

2   An OS map has a map ratio of $1:50\,000$.
    (a) What distance, in metres, does 1 cm on the map represent?
    (b) How far apart are two villages that are 30 cm apart on the map?
    (c) How wide is a river that is 0.75 cm wide on the map?
    (d) Two towns are 5 km apart. How far apart would they be on the map?

3   John wishes to draw a scale diagram of a triangular field ABC.

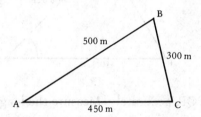

If he uses a scale of $1\,\text{cm} \equiv 50\,\text{m}$ what will be the length in the drawing of
    (a) AB   (b) AC   (c) BC?

4

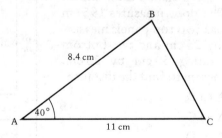

The sketch shows the positions of three towns Ampney, Buckton and Cawley. Use this information to make an accurate scale drawing. If 1 cm represents 1 km how far is it
    (a) from Buckton to Cawley,
    (b) from Cawley to Ampney?

5 The diagram is a scale drawing of part of a village.

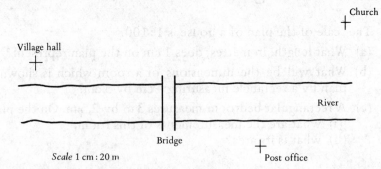

Scale 1 cm : 20 m

(a) How wide is the river?

(b) How far is the village hall from the church?

(c) How far is it from the church to the post office
(i) as the crow flies,   (ii) on foot using the bridge?

6

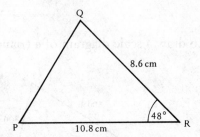

Draw triangle PQR accurately. Measure the length of PQ and the size of PQ̂R.

7 Use a scale of 1 cm to represent 10 cm to draw an accurate scale diagram of the panelled door shown opposite. The door measures 195 cm by 80 cm, has two top panels measuring 90 cm by 25 cm and two bottom panels measuring 50 cm by 25 cm. Use your diagram to find the distance

(a) from A to B,

(b) from A to C,

(c) from A to D.

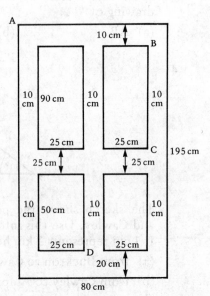

8

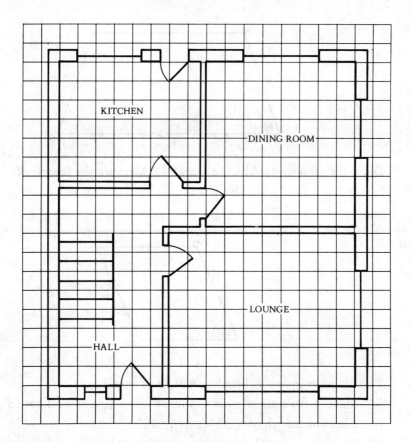

The plan of the ground floor of a house is drawn to a scale of 1 cm to 1 metre.

(a) What are the measurements of
    (i) the lounge,   (ii) the dining room,   (iii) the kitchen?

(b) What is the area of
    (i) the lounge,   (ii) the kitchen?

(c) Find the cost of carpeting the lounge at £20 per square metre.

(d) The cost of floor covering for the kitchen was £60. What is the price, per square metre, of this floor covering? Give your answer correct to the nearest £1.

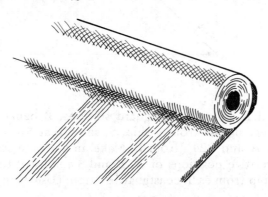

9

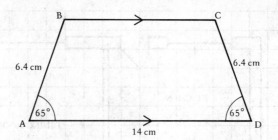

Draw the trapezium ABCD accurately. Measure the length of
(a) BC   (b) AC   (c) BD.

10

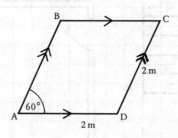

The diagram shows a rhombus ABCD of side 2 m.
(a) Make a drawing of this rhombus using a scale of 1 cm to 25 cm.
(b) Find the length of (i) AC (ii) BD.
(c) Show in a sketch how three such rhombuses can be arranged to form a regular hexagon.

11

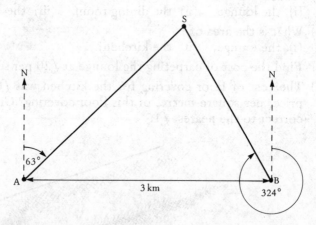

A and B are two coastguard stations, B being 3 km due east of A. Distress signals from a ship, S, show that S is on a bearing of 063° from A and 324° from B. Make an accurate scale diagram to show the relative positions of A, B and S and use it to find the distance of the ship from each coastguard station. (Use 4 cm to represent 1 km.)

12

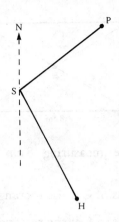

From the school, S, the post office, P, is 500 m on a bearing of 053°, while the village hall, H, is 750 m on a bearing of 164°. Draw a scale diagram using 1 cm to represent 50 m. Hence find the distance and bearing of the post office from the village hall.

13

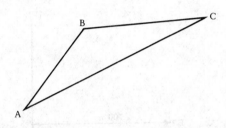

A, B and C represent three trees in a field. From A, B is 150 m on a bearing of 036°, and from B, C is 250 m on a bearing of 082°. Draw a scale diagram, taking 1 cm to represent 25 m. Hence find the distance and bearing of

(a) C from A,   (b) A from C.

14

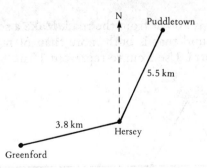

From Hersey, the village of Puddletown is 5.5 km in a direction N26°E and the town of Greenford is 3.8 km in a direction S75°W. Make a scale drawing of the relative positions of the three places. Use 2 cm to represent 1 km. Use your drawing to find the distance and direction of Puddletown from Greenford.

15

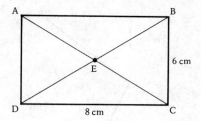

ABCD is a rectangle measuring 8 cm by 6 cm, whose diagonals intersect at E.

(a) Describe the locus of C if the rectangle is rotated about A.

(b) Describe the locus of C if the rectangle is rotated about D.

(c) Describe the locus of B if the rectangle is rotated about E.

(d) Describe the locus of E if the rectangle is rotated about C.
(All rotations take place in the plane of the rectangle.)

16

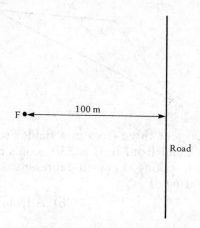

A farm, F, is 100 m from the road. Make a scale drawing to show the area of ground that is both more than 60 m from the road and 60 m from the farm. Use 1 cm to represent 10 m.

17

A prism with a cross-section in the form of an equilateral triangle is turned about successive edges through C and B until A is once again at its original level. Sketch the locus of A.

18 The map shows a small area in the Cotswolds.

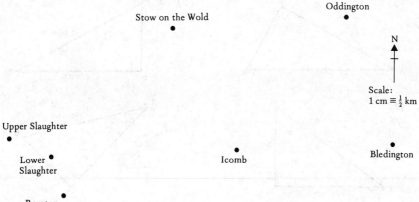

(a) A helicopter flies directly from Bourton-on-the-Water to Oddington.

How far and on what three-figure bearing does the helicopter fly?

(b) The helicopter then flies from Oddington to Icomb.
   (i) On what three-figure bearing does it fly?
   (ii) If this flight takes 4 minutes, find the average speed of the helicopter for this flight. Give your answer in kilometres per hour correct to the nearest 5 km/h.

Pythagoras' Theorem   11

1 ABC is a right-angled triangle with $\widehat{C} = 90°$.

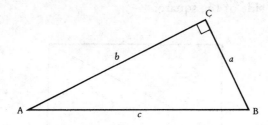

Use the result of Pythagoras to find the missing side if
(a) $a = 3$ cm, $b = 4$ cm   (b) $b = 8$ cm, $c = 10$ cm
(c) $a = 1.5$ cm, $c = 2.5$ cm   (d) $b = 2.8$ cm, $c = 3.5$ cm
(e) $a = 33$ cm, $b = 44$ cm   (f) $b = 12$ cm, $c = 13$ cm
(g) $a = 4$ cm, $c = 10.4$ cm   (h) $a = 1.9$ m, $b = 2.5$ cm
(i) $b = 14$ cm, $c = 21$ cm   (j) $b = 28.4$ cm, $c = 35.9$ cm

In questions 2 and 3 find the missing sides.

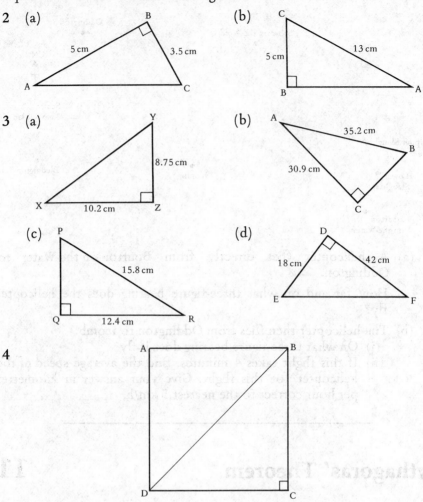

2 (a)

B

5 cm   3.5 cm

A   C

(b)

C

5 cm   13 cm

B   A

3 (a)

Y

8.75 cm

X   10.2 cm   Z

(b)

A

35.2 cm

B

30.9 cm

C

(c)

P

15.8 cm

Q   12.4 cm   R

(d)

D

18 cm   42 cm

E   F

4

A   B

D   C

The length of the diagonal of a square ABCD is 50 cm. Find the length of a side of the square.

5

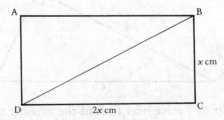

A   B

x cm

D $2x$ cm   C

ABCD is a rectangle in which BC = x cm and DC = $2x$ cm.

(a) Write down (i) BC² (ii) DC² in terms of x.

(b) If BD = 50 cm, form an equation in x and solve it to find the length of BC.

(c) What is the area of this rectangle?

46

6

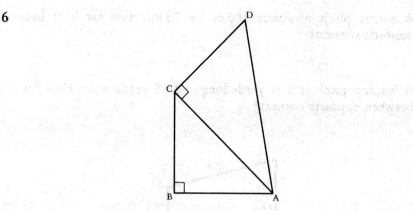

In the diagram AB = BC = CD = 10 cm. Find the length of
(a) AC   (b) AD.

7

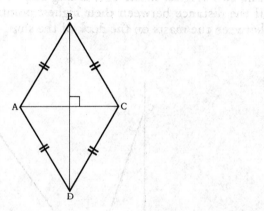

The diagonals of a rhombus are 7 cm and 16.8 cm long. Find the perimeter.

8

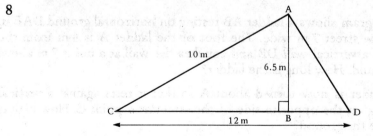

In the diagram AB represents a vertical flagstaff 6.5 m high. Restraining wires AC and AD are attached to the top of the flagstaff and to points C and D on the same level as B. If CD = 12 m and AC = 10 m find
(a) BC   (b) AD.

47

9 A soccer pitch measures 106 m by 70 m. How far is it between opposite corners?

10 A hockey pitch is 100 yards long and 55 yards wide. How far is it between opposite corners?

11

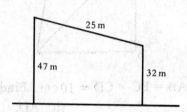

The two vertical masts of a sailing ship have heights 47 m and 32 m. If the distance between their highest points is 25 m find the distance between the masts on the deck of the ship.

12

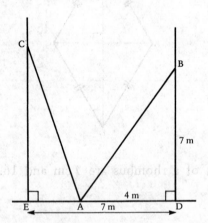

The diagram shows a ladder AB resting on horizontal ground DAE in a narrow street 7 m wide. The foot of the ladder A is 4 m from the base of a vertical wall DB and touches the wall at a point 7 m above the ground. How long is the ladder?

The ladder is now turned about A so that it rests against a vertical building on the opposite side of the street at a point C. How high is C above the ground?

13 From a point A a boy walks 350 metres due north to a point B. At B he turns east and walks 420 metres to C where he turns and walks 760 metres in a southerly direction to a fourth point D. How far is D from the starting point?

14

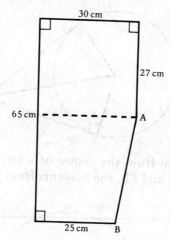

The diagram shows the section through a kitchen wall cupboard, AB representing the sliding glass door. Find AB correct to the nearest millimetre.

15

The figure shows the dimensions for a wooden book-end which is to be made by a form of 20 Year 8 pupils. Find

(a) its perimeter,

(b) its volume if the wood is uniformly 1.5 cm thick,

(c) the total volume of wood in the book ends, if each pupil of the form requires two of them.

16

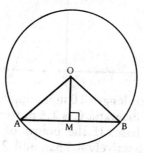

AB is a chord 24 cm long, in a circle centre O and radius 15 cm. If M is the midpoint of AB, find OM.

17

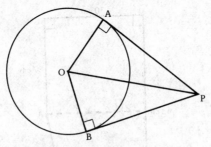

P is a point 26 cm from the centre of a circle of radius 10 cm. Find the lengths of PA and PB, the tangents from P to the circle.

18

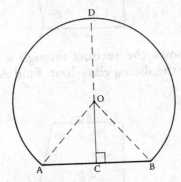

The diagram shows the cross-section of a tunnel which is part of a circle. The radius of the circle is 13 m and the width AB, of the tunnel at ground level, is 24 m. Find

(a) the height of O, the centre of the circle, above ground level,

(b) the height of the tunnel,

(c) the maximum width of the tunnel.

19

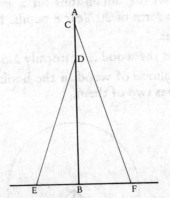

A vertical pole AB, of length 10 m is supported by two wires, CF and DE, as shown in the diagram. C is 1.5 m from the top of the pole, and D is 7 m from its base. If the points of attachment, E and F, at ground level are respectively 1.75 m and 2 m from the base B, calculate the total length of supporting wire used, in metres, giving your answer correct to one decimal place.

20 The diagonals of a picture frame are each 25 cm long. If the frame is twice as long as it is wide find its dimensions. Give each answer correct to 3 s.f.

Congruency and Similarity 12

In questions 1 to 4 determine whether or not the given pairs of triangles are congruent.

1

2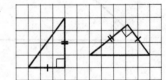

3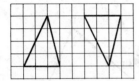

4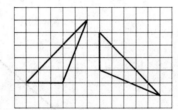

5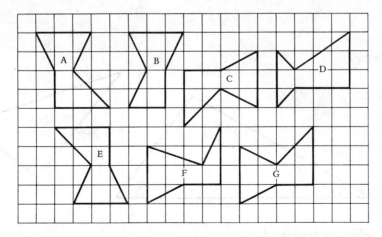

Which figures are congruent with A?

51

6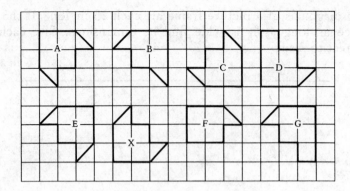

Which figures are congruent with X?

7 Triangles ABC and DEF are similar.

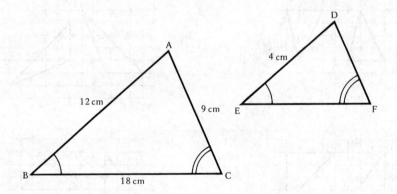

Find the length of
(a) DF   (b) EF.

8

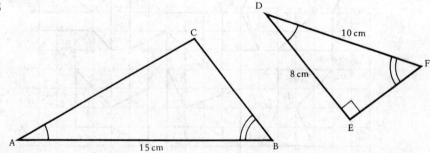

Find the length of
(a) EF   (b) AC   (c) BC.

9

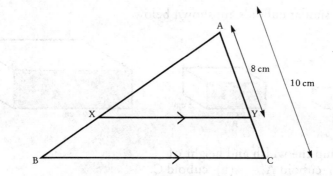

(a) If AX = 10 cm find the length of AB.

(b) If BC = 20 cm find the length of XY.

10

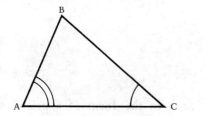

The area of △ABC is equal to four times the area of △DEF.

(a) If AC = 12 cm what is the length of DF?

(b) If EF = 5.5 cm what is the length of BC?

11

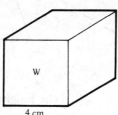
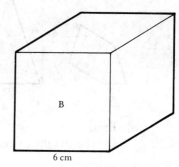

2 cm   4 cm   6 cm

Cubes of three sizes are coloured red (R) or white (W) or blue (B). The cubes are hollow with edges of 2 cm, 4 cm and 6 cm respectively.

(a) How many red cubes are required to fill
    (i) a white cube,   (ii) a blue cube?

(b) What is the largest number of white cubes that can be placed in a blue cube? How many red cubes are required to fill the remaining space?

12 Three similar cuboids are shown below.

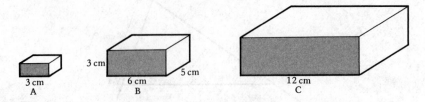

3 cm
A

3 cm
5 cm
6 cm
B

12 cm
C

(a) Find the width and height of
   (i) cuboid A,   (ii) cuboid C.

(b) For each cuboid find the area of the shaded face.

(c) How much more paint would be required to paint cuboid C than cuboid B?

13 Three similar ridge tents, each in the form of a prism, are shown below.

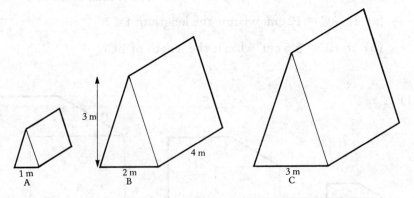

3 m

4 m

1 m
A

2 m
B

3 m
C

(a) Find
   (i) the height of tent A,   (ii) the height of tent C.

(b) Find
   (i) the length of tent A,   (ii) the length of tent C.

(c) Calculate the area of the vertical cross-section of
   (i) tent A,   (ii) tent B,   (iii) tent C.

(d) Find the volume of
   (i) tent A,   (ii) tent B,   (iii) tent C.

(e) Write down the ratio of the volume of tent A to tent B to tent C.

14

185 g
24 p

390 g
29 p

750 g
54 p

KDF dog food is sold in three similar cans. The prices and weights for each can are given in the sketches. Which size of can gives the best value for money? Explain your choice.

15

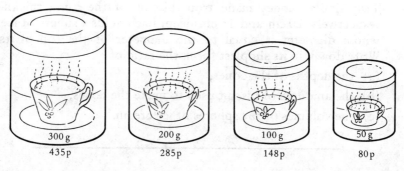

300 g
435 p

200 g
285 p

100 g
148 p

50 g
80 p

Coffee is sold in four different sizes, in jars that are mathematically similar. The weight and price of each jar is given with the sketches.

(a) Which jar would you buy to get the best value for money?

(b) Which jar gives you the most expensive coffee?

16

The ingredients for a rich fruit cake, which is to be baked in a 7-inch tin, include 10 oz currants, 7 oz sultanas, 5 oz flour and 2 oz ground almonds. What quantities of these ingredients are required for baking a cake in a 10-inch tin? Assume that the two tins have the same depth.

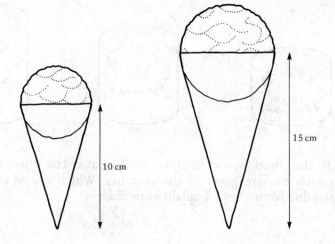

Two similar cones made from biscuit of the same thickness are respectively 10 cm and 15 cm deep. Each holds a sphere of ice cream whose diameter is equal to the diameter of the top of its cone. Write down, in its simplest form, the ratio of

(a) the depths of the cones,

(b) the amounts of biscuit used to make the cones,

(c) the volumes of the spheres of ice cream.

The Straight Line 13

1

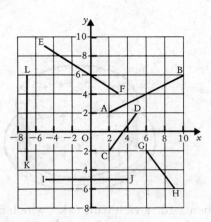

(a) Write down the coordinates of each of the lettered points.

(b) Write down the gradients of
    (i) AB   (ii) CD   (iii) EF   (iv) GH   (v) IJ   (vi) LK.

2 Draw axes for x and y from -10 to $+10$ using the same scale on both axes.

(a) Plot the points A(6, 3), B(5, 6), C(-3, 4) and D(-2, 1). What kind of quadrilateral is ABCD?

(b) Plot the points P(4, 2), Q(-1, 5), R(-6, 2) and S(4, -4). What kind of quadrilateral is PQRS?

(c) Plot the points E(-6, -6), F(-6, -3), G(4, 1) and H(4, -2). What kind of a quadrilateral is EFGH? Write down the gradient of (i) EH (ii) FG.

3 For each of the following straight line graphs write down

(i) the gradient of the line,

(ii) the coordinates of the point where it crosses the y-axis.

(a)

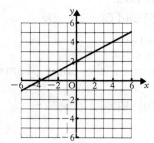

(b)

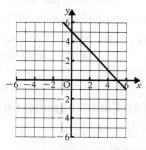

(c)

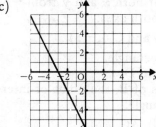

(d)

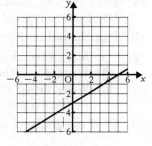

4 For each of the following straight line equations find

(i) the gradient of the line,

(ii) the coordinates of the point where it crosses the y-axis.

(a) $y = 2x + 6$ (b) $y = 3x - 7$

(c) $y = -5x + 2$ (d) $y = -\frac{1}{2}x + 3$

(e) $y = 5 - x$ (f) $y = 4 - 3x$

5 Find the equation of the straight line

(a) with gradient 4, which crosses the y-axis at the point (0, 5),

(b) with gradient -3, which crosses the y-axis at the point (0, 2),

(c) with gradient $\frac{1}{2}$, which crosses the y-axis at the point (0, -4),

(d) with gradient $-\frac{3}{2}$, which crosses the y-axis at the point (0, $\frac{1}{2}$).

6 (a) Draw x- and y-axes for values of both x and y from -6 to 8. Use 1 cm to represent 1 unit on both axes.
   (b) Plot the points A(4, -2), B(6, 6) and C(-2, 4).
   (c) (i) Mark the point D such that ABCD is a parallelogram (i.e. DA and CB are parallel, and AB and DC are parallel).
       (ii) Write down the coordinates of D.
       (iii) Draw the diagonals AC and BD. Hence write down the coordinates of E, the point of intersection of AC and BD.
   (d) (i) How many axes of symmetry does ABCD have?
       (ii) What special name is given to this parallelogram?
   (e) Find the gradient of (i) AB (ii) CB.

7 (a) Draw x- and y-axes for values of both x and y from -3 to 6. Use 2 cm to represent 1 unit on both axes.
   (b) Plot the points A(5, 5), B(-2, 5) and C(-2, -2).
   (c) (i) Mark D so that ABCD is a square.
       (ii) Write down the coordinates of D.
       (iii) Write down the coordinates of the point of intersection of the diagonals.
   (d) Find the gradient of (i) CA (ii) BD.

8 (a) Draw x- and y-axes for values of both x and y from -8 to 10. Use 1 cm to represent 1 unit on both axes.
   (b) Plot the points A(-2, 9), B(6, 9) and C(6, -5).
   (c) (i) Mark D so that ABCD is a rectangle.
       (ii) Write down the coordinates of D.
       (iii) Write down the coordinates of E, the point of intersection of the diagonals of the rectangle.
   (d) Find the gradient of (i) DB (ii) AC.

9 Sketch the graphs of the straight lines whose equations are
   (a) $x = 3$ (b) $y = 4$
   (c) $x = -2$ (d) $y = 2x$
   (e) $y = 2x + 3$ (f) $y = x - 4$
   (g) $y = 4 - x$ (h) $y = -x - 4$

10 Sketch the graphs of the straight lines whose equations are
   (a) $x + y = 1$ (b) $y - x = 3$
   (c) $x + 2y = 4$ (d) $x - y = 2$
   (e) $3x + y = 6$ (f) $x - 2y = 6$
   (g) $x + y = 3$ (h) $y - 3x = 9$

11 Pair up the graphs given below with the equations

(a) $y = x$

(b) $y = 2x + 4$

(c) $x + 2y = 2$

(d) $x + y + 1 = 0$

A
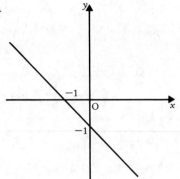

B
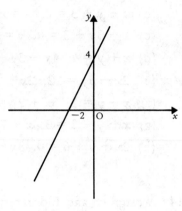

C
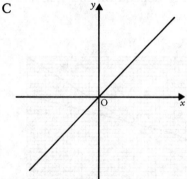

D
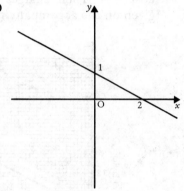

12 The table shows the marks of eight pupils in two tests.

Pupil	A	B	C	D	E	F	G	H
Science mark	43	25	56	65	29	60	10	45
Geography mark	62	40	80	94	49	89	23	71

On graph paper construct a scatter diagram for this data. Use 2 cm to represent 10 marks on both axes.

(a) Draw a line of best fit.

(b) Use your line to estimate
    (i) the science mark of a pupil who scored 50 in geography,
    (ii) the geography mark of a pupil who scored 50 in science,
    (iii) the geography mark of a pupil who scored 0 in science,
    (iv) the science mark of a pupil who scored 100 in geography.

13 Solve graphically the following pairs of simultaneous equations. Take values of x and y from -8 to 8. Use 1 cm to represent 1 unit on both axes.

(a) $y = x$, $3x + 2y = 6$

(b) $x + y + 3 = 0$, $y = x - 2$

(c) $x - 3y + 3 = 0$, $y = x$

(d) $x + y = 4$, $4x - 3y - 6 = 0$

(e) $2x - 3y = 12$, $2x + y = 8$

(f) $x + y = 1$, $3x + 2y = 6$

(g) $x - y + 2 = 0$, $x + 2y = 8$

(h) $2x + y + 6 = 0$, $3x - 4y + 4 = 0$

14 Westgrove and Floorcraft are two firms that specialise in laying floor coverings. Their charges for laying depend on the area laid and are given on the accompanying graph.

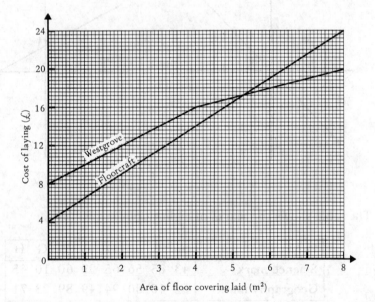

(a) How much would each company charge for laying 4 m² of floor covering?

(b) What area would Floorcraft lay for £20?

(c) Which company is the cheaper for laying (i) 5 m² (ii) 7 m²?

(d) What is the smallest *whole number* of square metres that Westgrove would lay at a lower price than Floorcraft?

(e) What is the largest *whole number* of square metres that Floorcraft would lay at a lower price than Westgrove?

15 Details of the last quarterly telephone bills in three adjacent houses are given in the table.

House number	No. of units used (x)	Total cost ($£P$)
1	780	62.90
2	400	42
3	1140	82.70

Draw a straight line graph to represent this information using $1\,\text{cm} \equiv 100$ units on the horizontal x-axis and $1\,\text{cm} \equiv £5$ on the vertical axis. Use your graph to find

(a) the gradient and intercept on the P-axis,

(b) the cost of one unit,

(c) the quarterly rental charge.

16 (a) (i) Jones Bros. hire out vans at a basic charge of £10 plus a further 40p per kilometre. If $£C$ is the total hire charge when the van travels x km, copy and complete the following table.

x	0	50	100	150	200
C			50		90

(ii) Draw a graph to represent this data using 2 cm to represent 25 km on the x-axis and 2 cm to represent £10 on the C-axis.

(iii) Use your graph to find the hire charge for a distance of (1) 10 km (2) 135 km.

(b) (i) Smith & Son Ltd hire out vans at a basic charge of £25 plus a further charge of 30p per kilometre. If $£B$ is the total hire charge when the van travels x km, copy and complete the following table.

x	0	25	100	125	175
B		32.5	55		77.5

(ii) Use the same axes to draw the graph to show how B varies with x.

(c) For what distance do both firms make the same hire charge?

(d) Ted Morris needs to hire a van for a 180 km journey. Which firm should he hire from? How much will he save?

Travel Graphs

1

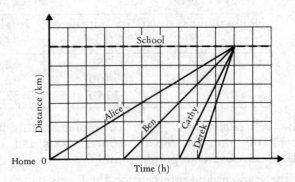

The graph shows the journeys of four pupils to school. One of them cycles, one of them comes by bus, one of them is brought by car and one of them walks.

(a) Use the graph to decide how each pupil comes to school.

(b) If the cyclist averages 10 km/h what is the average speed of
   (i) the walker,   (ii) the pupil who comes by car?

2   The graph shows the total mileage of dual carriageway in use in Westshire at the end of each year from 1990 to 1995. The figure for 1999 is the projected figure.

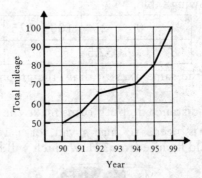

(a) How many miles were completed in (i) 1991   (ii) 1995?

(b) The graph suggests that the local authority will provide more miles of dual carriageway in the next few years than they have in the past. Do you agree? Give reasons for your answer.

62

3   The graph shows Matthew's journey home after leaving work.

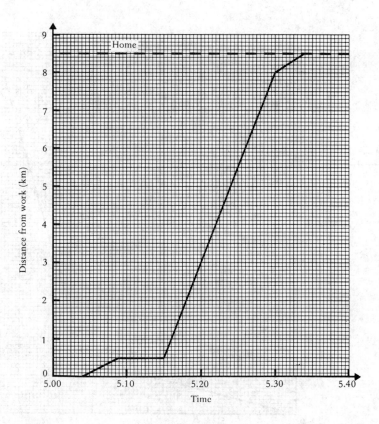

(a)   (i)   What time did Matthew leave work?
      (ii) How far did he walk to the bus stop?
      (iii) How long did it take him?
      (iv) Find his average walking speed in km/h.

(b)   How long did he have to wait for the bus?

(c)   (i)   How far did he travel on the bus?
      (ii) How long did the bus ride last?
      (iii) What was the average speed of the bus while Matthew was travelling on it?

(d)   (i)   What time did Matthew arrive home?
      (ii) How long did his journey from work take him?
      (iii) What is the distance from his place of work to his home?
      (iv) What was his average speed for the whole journey?

4   The graph shows Alyson's journey from home to school. She walked to the bus stop and had to wait until the school bus arrived.

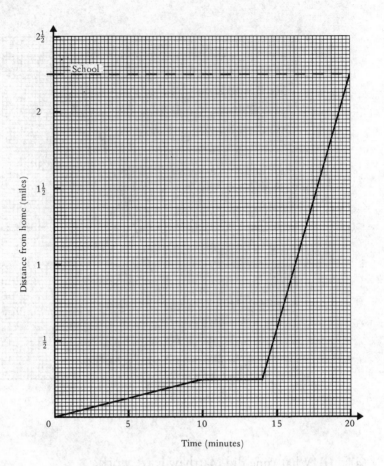

Use the graph to answer the following questions.

(a) What is the distance from Alyson's home to school?

(b) How long did she take to walk to the bus stop?

(c) How far was the bus stop from her home?

(d) What was the average walking speed in m.p.h.? Is this a good walking pace?

(e) How long did she have to wait for the bus?

(f) How far did she travel on the bus?

(g) How long did the bus ride take her?

(h) At what average speed, in m.p.h., did the bus travel?

(i) What was the average speed for the whole journey from home to school?

5

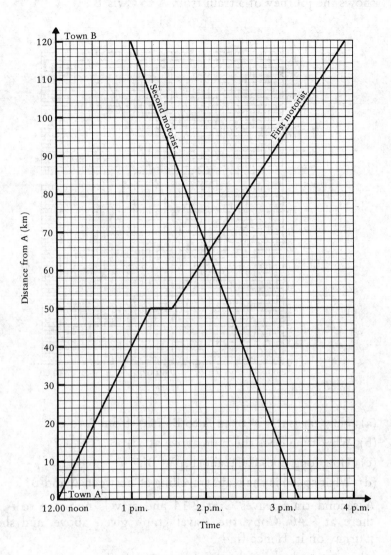

The travel graph shows the journeys of two motorists. The first leaves town A at 12 noon and travels to town B, while the second travels from town B to town A. Use the graph to determine

(a) the first motorist's time of arrival at B,

(b) the speed of the first motorist for
    (i) the first part of the journey,   (ii) the whole journey,

(c) the second motorist's average speed,

(d) when and where the two pass.

6 A, B and C are three stations on a railway line. The travel graph shows the journey of a train from A to C via B.

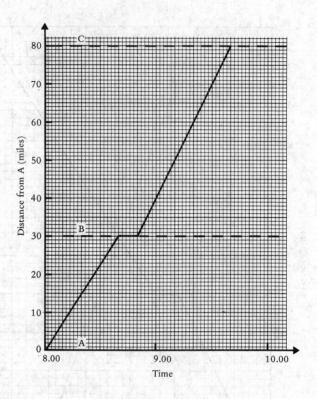

(a) How far is it (i) from A to B (ii) from A to C?

(b) What time does the train arrive at (i) B (ii) C?

(c) How long does the train stop at B?

(d) What speed is the train travelling at between A and B?

A second train leaves C at 8.14 and travels non-stop to A arriving there at 9.46. Copy the travel graph given above, and show this journey on it. Hence find

(e) when and where the two trains pass,

(f) their distance apart at 9.10,

(g) the average speed of the second train.

7 Peter and David are two school friends who live in Elmwood and Oakwood, two towns which are 18 km apart. On the first Monday of the summer holiday Peter leaves Elmwood at 9.12 a.m. and walks at a steady pace of 7 km/h directly to Oakwood.

David's father leaves Oakwood at 9.40 a.m. and cycles towards Elmwood. He travels for the first 20 minutes at a steady speed of 21 km/h, but then has a small problem with his bicycle which causes him to reduce his speed, finally arriving in Elmwood at 10.44 a.m.

Taking 6 cm to represent 1 h on the time-axis, and 1 cm to represent 1 km on the distance-axis, draw travel graphs to represent the two journeys. Use your graphs to find

(a) Peter's time of arrival at Oakwood,

(b) David's father's average speed for the slower part of his journey,

(c) when and where they pass,

(d) their distance apart at 10.20 a.m.

8   John sets out at noon from his home village of Atley, to call at Bentham which is 16 km away, before going on to Cottle, a village which is 9 km beyond Bentham. He walks for 1 h at 6 km/h, then rests for 20 minutes before running the remaining distance to his cousin's home at Bentham at 10 km/h. Here he chats for 4 minutes before leaving on a borrowed bicycle, cycling to Cottle at an average speed of 16 km/h.

Draw a travel graph to represent John's journey taking 6 cm ≡ 1 h and 4 cm ≡ 5 km. Use your graph to find his time of arrival at Cottle.

In the meantime his friend Tim leaves Cottle at 12.40 p.m. and cycles leisurely to Atley at a steady 12 km/h. Show this on the same graph and hence find

(a) when and where the two pass,

(b) Tim's time of arrival at Atley,

(c) their distance apart at 1.34 p.m.

67

9 The graph represents a 1000 metre race between Richard and Steve.

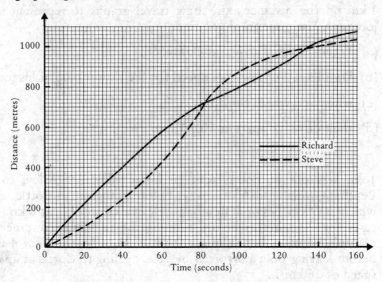

(a) How far apart are the two runners after 40 seconds?
(b) Who is leading for the first part of the race?
(c) After how many seconds does the lead change hands?
(d) Who won the race and by how many seconds?

Income and Expenditure   15

1 Fred Brown's time-sheet for a week is shown below.

Name: Fred Brown
Works Number: 1098
Week Ending: 17 April 1996

Day	Clocked in at	Clocked out at
Mon.	07.00	16.00
Tue.	07.00	16.00
Wed.	07.15	18.15
Thur.	07.00	16.00
Fri.	07.00	16.00

(a) What seems to be the time at which Fred is due to start work?
(b) What is the length of his normal working day?
(c) Assuming that he has 1 hour for lunch each day (unpaid), how many hours make up his basic week?
(d) How many hours of overtime has he worked?

2   George Sale earns £3.50 per hour for a 40-hour week. Calculate his gross weekly wage.

3   Alma Hird earns £3.25 per hour for a 35-hour week. Calculate her gross weekly wage.

4   Barry Cole works a basic week of $37\frac{1}{2}$ hours and is paid £5.20 per hour. Calculate his gross weekly wage.

5   The wages slip shown below is to be completed for a factory worker. He works a basic 38-hour week at £6.80 per hour and $2\frac{1}{2}$ hours overtime every week at time-and-a-half.

Name: Able Man		Works No. 3475		Date: 21.02.96	
Nat. Ins. No. ZP 743261 A					
Hours		Payments		Deductions	
Basic	at $1\frac{1}{2}$	Basic pay £		National Insurance £	
38	$2\frac{1}{2}$	Overtime £		Income Tax £	
		GROSS PAY £		Total deductions £	
				NET PAY £	

(a) Calculate
   (i) his basic pay,
   (ii) his overtime pay,
  (iii) his gross pay for the week.

Copy the wages slip and enter these details on it.

(b) If National Insurance is 2% of the first £265 plus 10% of the remainder of his weekly pay, calculate his National Insurance contribution and enter it on the wages slip. Give your answer correct to the nearest penny.

(c) Income Tax is not paid on National Insurance contributions nor on the first £65 of his weekly income.
   (i) Calculate the amount of his pay on which he must pay Income Tax.
   (ii) Calculate the total Income Tax he pays if the rate of tax is 20 p in the £.
  (iii) Complete his wages slip.

(d) What percentage of his gross pay does he actually receive? Give your answer correct to the nearest whole number.

(e) How much less take-home pay would he have if the tax rate was raised from 20 p to 25 p?

6 Richard Elder's time-sheet for a week shows that he worked as follows.

	In	Out
Mon.	7.58 a.m.	4.28 p.m.
Tue.	8.00 a.m.	4.30 p.m.
Wed.	8.04 a.m.	4.31 p.m.
Thur.	8.12 a.m.	5.45 p.m.
Fri.	7.59 a.m.	6.15 p.m.
Sat.	8.05 a.m.	12 noon

Richard is due to start work each day at 8.00 a.m. and to finish at 4.30 p.m. He is not paid for arriving early but loses 15 minutes any day he is more than 5 minutes late. He also loses 15 minutes if he leaves before 4.30 p.m. but is paid at time-and-a-half for each complete 15 minutes he works overtime – any work on Saturday being counted as overtime. If the basic hourly rate is £4.80, calculate his wage for the week.

7 The following table shows the number of articles produced by four factory workers each day for a week. If each person is paid 16 p for each article up to 200 per day and 24 p for each article above 200 per day, calculate each worker's earnings for the week.

	Mon.	Tue.	Wed.	Thur.	Fri.	Sat.
Mr Hollands	296	202	264	276	243	–
Miss Bennett	284	198	273	–	176	234
Mrs Hogan	217	254	244	175	269	–
Mr Hyde	273	284	180	233	245	–

8 Barry Price gets paid 5 p for every article he produces above 600 in a week. In addition he receives a guaranteed wage of £85. The following table shows the number of articles produced each day for a week.

Mon.	Tue.	Wed.	Thur.	Fri.
164	173	154	182	176

Calculate his earnings.

9 Carl Humphreys receives a basic monthly wage of £450 together with commission at 2% of the value of his sales. Calculate his gross annual earnings in a year when he sells goods to the value of £550 000.

10   Two brothers George and Henry Patterson both work as salesmen for the same company, but in different sections. Each receives a basic monthly wage of £130 plus commission as follows.

George: 2% on all sales above £10 000 each month
Henry: 1½% on all sales above £2000 each week

During a four-week month their respective sales figures were

George: £7420, £8680, £12 000, £9450
Henry: £4930, £1950, £15 170, £11 000

Which brother has the better month and by how much?

11   The cash price for a video recorder is £400. If bought on credit terms over twenty-four months the cost is £100 more than the cash price. The credit agreement requires a deposit plus twenty-four monthly payments of £17. Find

(a) the deposit, if bought on credit terms,

(b) the extra cost if bought on credit, expressed as a percentage of the cash price,

(c) the cash price in a sale where all goods are marked down by 25%.

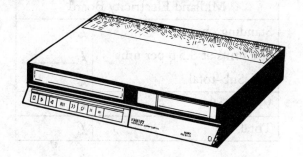

12   The cash price of a washing machine is £276. It can be bought on credit terms by paying a deposit of one third of the cash price followed by 36 monthly payments of £6.64.

(a) How much is the deposit?

(b) What is the total cost of buying the machine on credit?

(c) How much more is the credit price than the cash price?

13   A man's suit can be bought for £126 cash or for a deposit of £42 plus 12 monthly instalments of £7.56.

(a) How much more does the suit cost if bought on the instalment plan compared with the cash price?

(b) Express the additional cost as a percentage of the cash price.

71

14 A motorcycle is offered for sale at £560. If bought on credit terms, a deposit of $\frac{1}{4}$ is required together with 24 monthly payments of £21.49. Calculate the difference between the cash price and the credit terms price.

15 (a) The positions of the hands on the dials of an electricity meter are shown in the diagram. Write down the meter reading.

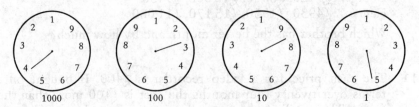

(b) If 560 units of electricity are used during the following twelve weeks, write down the new meter reading. Show this new reading on a set of dials.

(c) Mr Foulds has to pay a standing charge of £11.80 plus 8.5p for each unit of electricity used. Complete his quarterly bill.

Midland Electricity Board	
Standing charge	£
560 units at 8.5 p per unit	£_____
Sub-total	£
VAT at 8%	£
Total	£

16 Jane Lock uses White Meter electricity for her storage heaters and for heating domestic water. Her quarterly bill shows the following details.

Meter reading		Units used	Unit charges		£
Present	Previous		8.5 p	4.74 p	
33 634	32 617	1017	1017		
Quarterly standing charge					11.50
39 543	38 301	1242		1242	
Time switch					2.40
			Sub-total		
			VAT at 8%		
			Amount due		

Complete the table and hence calculate the amount due.

17

```
┌─────────────────────────────────────────────────────────────────────┐
│  Midland Electricity Board                                            │
│                                                                       │
│  Account number    4274  3341                                         │
│                                                                       │
│  Mr P.R. Brown                        Meter reading date   12 Nov. 95 │
│  42 Chipfold Road                     Invoice date         14 Nov. 95 │
│  Coventry                                                             │
│                                                                       │
│  Previous meter reading    58916                                      │
│  Present meter reading     59813                                      │
│                                                                       │
│       Units consumed   [          ]                                   │
│                                                                       │
│  Cost of [            ]  units at 9 pence per unit    £ [      ]       │
│                                                                       │
│                        Quarterly standing charge     £ 12.40          │
│                                                                       │
│                                     Sub-total    £ [      ]            │
│                                                                       │
│                                   VAT at 8%      £ [      ]            │
│                                                                       │
│                                       Total      £ [      ]            │
│                                                                       │
└─────────────────────────────────────────────────────────────────────┘
```

(a) Complete this electricity bill by filling in the boxes.

(b) The meter is read every three months and was read again on 12 Feb 96, when the reading was 60 811. How many units had been used
   (i) for the three months up to 12 Feb 96,
   (ii) for the half year up to 12 Feb 96?

18 How many hours will each of the following appliances run on 1 unit of electricity? (1 unit $= 1$ kW h.)
  (a) a 100 W lamp,   (b) a 12 W lamp,
  (c) a 2 kW fire,   (d) a 500 W iron,
  (e) a 2.5 kW kettle.

19 Calculate the total cost of using the following appliances at 7.54 p per unit, i.e. 1 kW h, plus VAT at 8%.

        A 3 kW fire for 26 hours.
        Eight 100 W lamps, each for 38 hours.
        A 750 W iron for 4 hours.
        A 350 W television set for 45 hours.

Give your answer correct to the nearest penny.

20 Between 5 April and 6 July Eddy's telephone bill showed that he had used 846 charge units at 4.5p per unit. If the quarterly standing charge was £19 and VAT was added to the total at $17\frac{1}{2}$%, calculate his telephone bill for the quarter. Calculate, correct to the nearest 10p, the average weekly cost of the telephone.

21 Joe travels 17 850 km in a year on his motorcycle. If it averages 21 km to the litre, calculate how much he spends on petrol when petrol costs 60 p per litre. If petrol amounts to 25% of the total costs, how much per kilometre does his motorcycle cost him over the year? Give your answer in pence correct to three significant figures.

22 The cost of running Mandy's car for a year, excluding servicing and repairs is: road tax £135, insurance £182, depreciation £570, petrol 1650 litres at 53 p per litre.

In a year when she travelled 30 000 kilometres, she estimates that motoring, including servicing and repairs, averaged out at 6.2 p per kilometre. How much did she spend on servicing and repairs?

23 A property valued at £80 000 is insured at a rate of £1 per £1000 by a policy which is index linked. If the inflation rate is 10%, calculate the annual premium

(a) now,   (b) in 1 years time,   (c) in 2 years time.

24 My basic premium for fully comprehensive cover for my car is £400. A reduction of $12\frac{1}{2}$% of this premium is allowed because I agree to pay the first £50 costs for each and every claim. No claim discounts are allowed on the balance. How much will I be asked to pay if I am

(a) on 40% NCD,   (b) on full 60% NCD?

25 £1500 may be borrowed under two different schemes.

Scheme A: Repayment of £24.80 per month spread over 15 years.

Scheme B: Repayment of £22.75 per month for the first 5 years and then £27.08 per month for the next 10 years.

(a) Calculate the total amount repaid under Scheme A.

(b) How much more (or less) is paid under Scheme B than under Scheme A over the 15 years?

26 The salad cream in jar A has a mass of 486 g and costs 70 p, while that in jar B has a mass of 1 kg and costs £1.42. Find

(a) the cost of 1 gram of salad cream from jar A,

(b) the cost of one gram of salad cream from jar B.

Give each answer in pence correct to two decimal places. Which is the better buy?

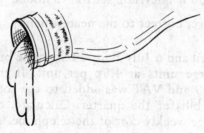

27 Peggy Rees orders some books from a mail order firm. Here is her incomplete order form.

Membership No. 274 803528033				
Cat. no.	No. of copies	Title	Price per copy	Total price
B426	1	*The Other Side of the Moon*	£6.95	
B109	2	*Whicker's New World*	£7.95	
B378	3	*Kommando*	£8.75	
			Postage	£2.75
			Total amount	

Complete this form.

Area and Volume   **16**

1   Find the area of each of the following figures.

(a)

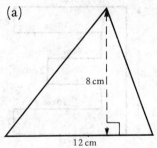

(b)

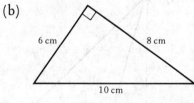

(c)

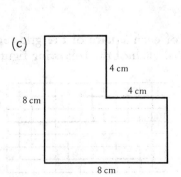

(d)

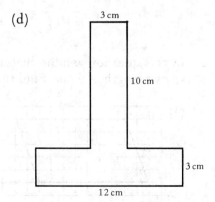

75

(e)

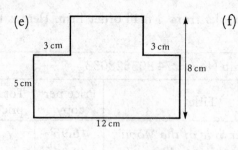

3 cm · 3 cm

5 cm

8 cm

12 cm

(f)

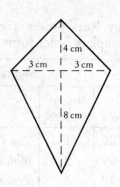

4 cm

3 cm · 3 cm

8 cm

(g)

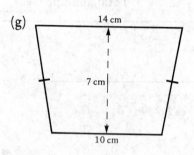

14 cm

7 cm

10 cm

(h)

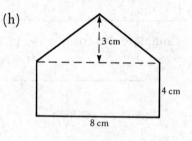

3 cm

4 cm

8 cm

(i)

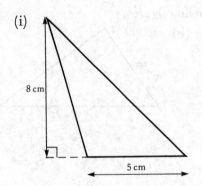

8 cm

5 cm

(j)

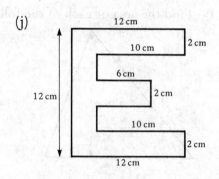

12 cm

10 cm

2 cm

6 cm

12 cm

2 cm

10 cm

2 cm

12 cm

2 In this question assume that a side of each square of the grid represents a length of 1 cm. Find the area of each of the following figures.

(a)

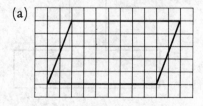

(b)

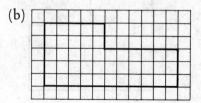

76

(c)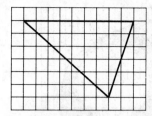

(d)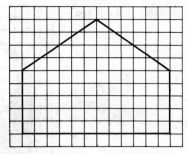

(e)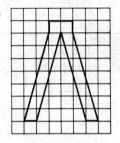

(f)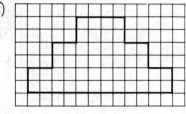

(g)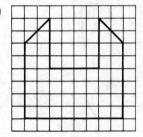

(h)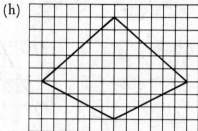

3   The following shapes are from everyday life. By counting squares and using the given scale, find the area of each.

(a) A lake

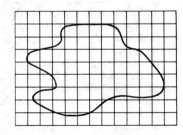

1 square represents 1 km²

(b) An oil seal

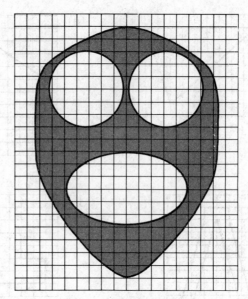

1 square represents 1 cm²

(c) A field

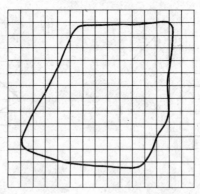

1 square represents 10 m²

(d) The cross-section of a tunnel

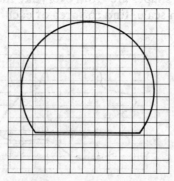

1 square represents 4 m²

(e) A green on the golf course

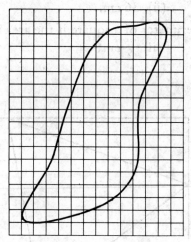

1 square represents 9 m²

(f) The cross-section of an egg

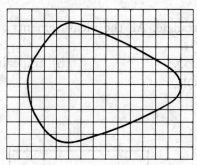

1 square represents 0.25 cm²

4

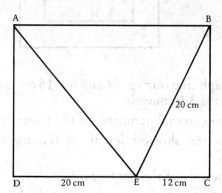

ABCD is a rectangle. Find the area of

(a) △BCE   (b) △ADE   (c) △ABE.

5 (a) Find the area of a square if the perimeter is
(i) 20 cm   (ii) 36 cm.

(b) Find the perimeter of a square if the area is
(i) 64 cm²   (ii) $\frac{25}{9}$ cm².

6

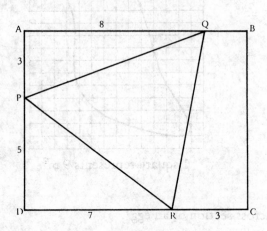

ABCD is a rectangle. All the measurements are in centimetres. Find the area of

(a) triangle APQ,   (b) trapezium BCRQ,

(c) triangle PQR.

7

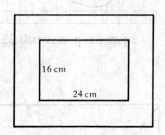

A photograph measuring 24 cm by 16 cm is to be framed using framing that is 3.5 cm wide.

(a) Find the external perimeter of the frame.

(b) What is the shortest length of framing required to make this frame?

(c) Find the area of the photograph.

(d) What area of wall does the framed photograph cover when it hangs on a wall?

(e) Find the area of the frame.

80

8

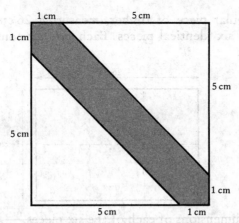

The diagram shows a square with a diagonal band, which is shaded. Find

(a) the side of the square,
(b) the area of the square,
(c) the total area unshaded,
(d) the area of the shaded band,
(e) the width of the band.

9

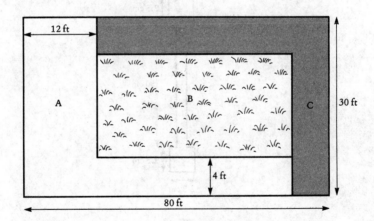

The diagram represents a rectangular garden measuring 80 ft by 30 ft made up of a paved area, A, a lawn, B, and a flower border, C, which is 4 feet wide everywhere.

(a) Area A is covered with square paving stones of side 2 feet. How many will be needed? How much will they cost if one stone costs £2.40?

(b) The lawn B is turfed at a cost of £2.45 per square yard. How much, correct to the nearest £10, will the turf cost?

(c) The border C is planted with small bushes each of which costs £2.50. If each bush requires 8 square feet of ground how many bushes will the border take? How much will these bushes cost?

10 A rectangular piece of timber, measuring 26 cm by 14 cm, is to be sawn into six identical pieces. Each saw cut consumes a 4 mm width of timber.

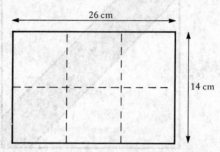

Find the dimensions of each of the six pieces.

11 The diagram below shows the cross-section through a domestic central heating radiator. The centre section is 50 cm high and 0.75 cm thick; at the top and bottom are squares of side 2.5 cm. Calculate the area of cross-section and hence find the volume of water, in litres, inside a radiator 2 m long.

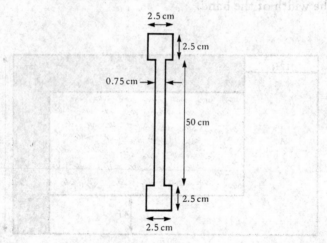

12

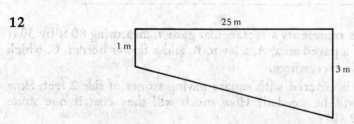

The depth of water in a swimming pool increases uniformly from 1 m at the shallow end to 3 m at the deep end. If the pool is 25 m long and 9 m wide, find the volume of water, in m³, in the pool when full. If it takes 8 hours to empty the pool completely, how long will it take until the floor becomes visible at the shallow end?

13

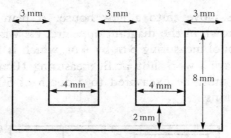

The diagram shows the cross-section of a piece of wooden channelling used for sliding glass doors in a kitchen wall cupboard. Calculate the volume of wood in a 2 m length, expressing your answer in cubic centimetres.

14

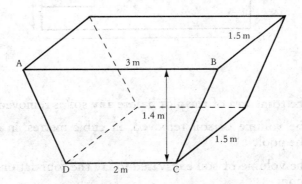

The diagram represents a builder's skip. The skip has a rectangular base measuring 2 m by 1.5 m, a rectangular open top measuring 3 m by 1.5 m, and is 1.4 m deep. The vertical sides are trapeziums and the sloping sides are rectangles.

(a) Find the area of the vertical side ABCD.

(b) Find the volume of waste in the skip when it is filled level with the top.

(c) By heaping it above the level of the top, a further 20% of waste material may be carried in the skip. How much does the skip hold when the waste is heaped in this way?

(d) If 1 m³ of waste has a mass of 600 kg, find the mass of waste in the skip when it is filled level with the top. Give your answer in tonnes.

15 The diagram shows the cross-section through a trench 12 m long which a gardener has prepared for planting his kidney beans. Find the volume of the soil removed.

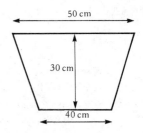

16 Carl Meyers moves into a new house. A plan of the rectangular
garden is shown in the diagram opposite. He wishes to have at A, a
swimming pool measuring 8 m by 4 m, which is 1.5 m deep. He also
wishes to have a workshop at B, measuring 10 m by 6 m, for which
the ground must be excavated to a depth of 50 cm in order to lay
the foundations.

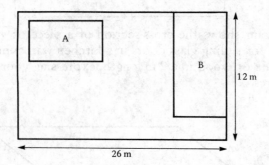

Find

(a) the total area of the plot before any soil is removed,

(b) the volume of soil removed, in cubic metres, in order to build
the pool,

(c) the volume of soil excavated to lay the foundations of the workshop,

(d) the combined ground area of A and B,

(e) the area of ground that is untouched.

The earth that is excavated from A and B is now laid evenly over the
remainder of the plot. By how much will the level of this area rise?

17 The diagram shows the cross-section of a kerb-stone 1 m long. Calculate its volume in cubic metres.

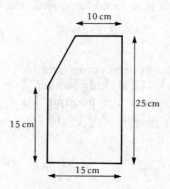

84

18 A cylinder lawn mower is 35 cm wide and has a diameter of 21 cm. Assuming that when it is used the cylinder revolves without slipping, calculate

(a) the distance moved forward by the mower for each revolution of the wheel,

(b) the number of complete revolutions required to mow a straight run of 99 m.

19 The minute hand of the town clock is 1.4 m long while the hour hand is 0.91 m long. How far does the tip of each hand move in one hour?

20 A goat is tethered by a rope 5.6 m long to the corner of a rectangular field. Find the length of the perimeter of the area of grass from which the goat may eat.

21 A circular pond has a diameter of 2 m. If its diameter is increased by 20 cm, by what length is its circumference increased? By how much should its original diameter be increased to double the area of the pool?

22 The total distance around a circular pond is 330 m. Find its radius.

23 A circular running track with an inner radius of 98 m is 7 m wide. How much further is it around the outer edge of the track than the inner?

24 A bicycle wheel is 66 cm in diameter. How many revolutions does it make per kilometre? Give your answer correct to the nearest whole number.

25 A circular fishpond of radius 3 m is surrounded by a path of uniform width 0.8 m. Find the area of the path.

26 A copper pipe has a bore of 21 mm and an external diameter of 25 mm. Find its cross-sectional area.

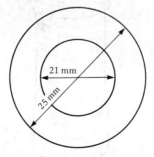

27 From a thin square metal plate of side 20 cm, four quadrants of a circle, each of radius 7 cm, are cut away at the corners. Find

(a) the area cut away,   (b) the area remaining.

28 A circular pond is 98 m in diameter. A fisherman, who is able to fish from anywhere along the edge of the pond, hopes to catch any fish coming within 14 m of the edge. Find the area of water for which

(a) the fish are outside the fisherman's range,

(b) the fisherman can expect to catch something.

29

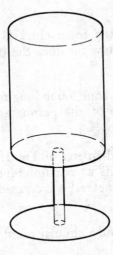

A cylindrical sherry glass has a diameter of 3.5 cm and is 6 cm high.

(a) Find the area of the glass in contact with sherry when it is filled to within 2 mm of the rim.

(b) Find the length of the longest cocktail stick that can be placed in the glass without protruding above the level of the rim.

30 A cylindrical pillar-box is 1.5 m high and has a diameter of 63 cm. Find the area that requires painting.

31 Find the volume of a can of baked beans which has a radius of 3.5 cm and is 11 cm high.

32 A cylindrical jug which is full of water has a radius of 6 cm and is 20 cm tall. Water from it is poured into cylindrical glasses of diameter 6 cm and height 10 cm. How many such glasses may be filled?

33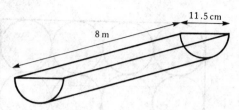

An 8 m length of guttering along the front of a house has a semi-circular cross-section of diameter 11.5 cm. If there are stoppers at each end, calculate the maximum volume of water in cubic metres that the guttering will hold at any one time.

34 A 1797 George III cartwheel penny is 3.2 mm thick and has a diameter of 3.5 cm. Find its volume. If a modern penny is 1.2 mm thick and 2.0 cm in diameter, how many are required to have the same volume as one cartwheel penny? Give your answer correct to the nearest whole number.

35 Wooden dowels with a diameter of 1 cm are made from lengths of timber with a square cross-section of side 1.2 cm. Find the percentage of wood wasted.

36 A 4 m length of tubular metal, external diameter 2 cm and 1.5 mm thick, is required to manufacture a school desk. Calculate the volume of metal used.

37 The diagram represents the vertical cross-section through a machine component. It shows a solid metal cylinder of diameter 5 cm and height 6 cm from which a cylinder of diameter 4 cm and depth 5 cm has been removed.

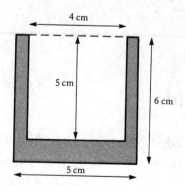

Calculate
(a) the volume of the cylinder before the hole is bored,
(b) the volume of metal removed,
(c) the mass of the finished component if the mass of 1 cm³ of the metal is 8.7 grams.

38 An open rectangular cardboard box is required to pack cylindrical tins. Each tin is 10 cm high and has a base diameter of 6 cm. The diagram shows one possible arrangement when the tins are packed 12 at a time.

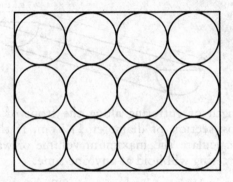

Find

(a) the length and breadth of the box,

(b) the capacity of the box,

(c) the volume of one of the tins,

(d) the amount of space in the box that is unused,

(e) the area of card used to make the box. (Ignore overlaps.)

Another packaging manufacturer suggested packing the tins in two layers with six tins on the base, arranged 2 × 3, and six tins placed on top of these.

(f) Would these boxes require a different amount of cardboard from the boxes used in the first part of the question?

(g) Would there, in percentage terms, be any difference in the amount of space wasted?

Nets and Solids   17

1 How many (i) edges, (ii) vertices, (iii) faces, has
   (a) a square pyramid,   (b) a tetrahedron,
   (c) a cuboid,   (d) a triangular prism?

2 Draw an accurate net for
   (a) a cube of side 3 cm,
   (b) a regular tetrahedron, each edge of which measures 3 cm,
   (c) a cuboid measuring 5 cm × 4 cm × 3 cm.

3

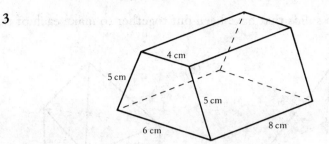

(a) Sketch a net for this trapezoidal prism.

(b) How many planes of symmetry does this solid have?

4 Complete each of the following statements.

(a) Apart from the square base the net of a square pyramid is made up of four _____ .

(b) The net of a cuboid is made up of _____ rectangles.

(c) The net of a triangular prism is made up of _____ triangles and _____ rectangles.

(d) The net of a cube consists of _____ squares.

5 Name the shape that can be made from each of the following nets.

(a)

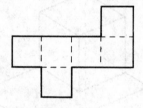

(b)

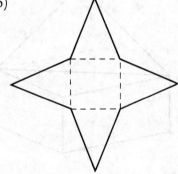

(c)

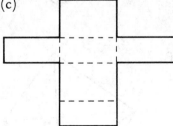

(d)

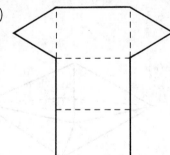

(e)

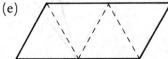

(f)

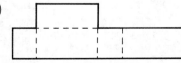

89

6 Name the two solids that have been put together to make each of the following shapes.

(a)

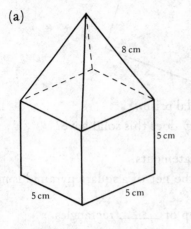

8 cm
5 cm
5 cm 5 cm

(b)

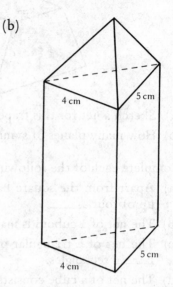

4 cm 5 cm
5 cm
4 cm 5 cm

(c)

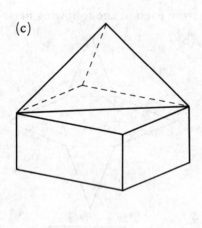

(d)

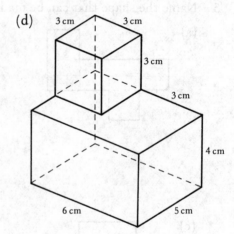

3 cm 3 cm
3 cm
3 cm
4 cm
6 cm 5 cm

(e)

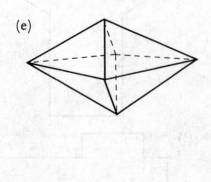

(f)

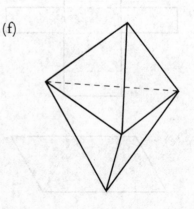

7   The surface area of a cube is 216 cm².

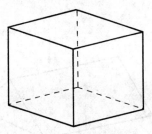

(a) (i) How many vertices does it have?
    (ii) How many edges does it have?
    (iii) How many faces does it have?

(b) Find
    (i)   the length of an edge,
    (ii) the volume of the cube,
    (iii) the total length of all its edges.

8   The diagram shows an open rectangular box.

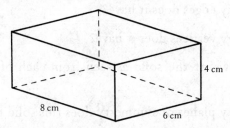

(a) Draw an accurate net for this box when the four sides are folded backwards into the same plane as the base.

(b) Sketch a net for this box such that just one side is joined to the base.

9   The sketch shows a solid made from a cuboid surmounted by a pyramid.

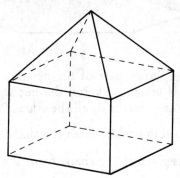

(a) How many faces does the solid have?
(b) How many edges does it have?
(c) How many vertices does it have?

10 This sketch shows a uniform triangular prism fitting exactly on top of a cuboid.

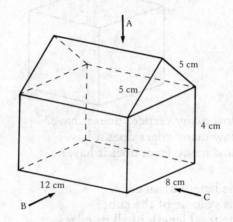

(a) How many faces does the solid have?

(b) How many edges does it have?

(c) How many vertices does it have?

(d) Draw views of the solid as seen from each of the directions A, B and C.

(e) How many planes of symmetry does this solid have?

11

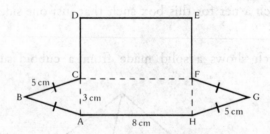

(a) This drawing shows part of the net of a shape, one rectangular face, AJIH, is missing. Sketch the net and add the missing face. Mark the measurements of all the edges on your completed net.

(b) Which points join with B when the shape is formed?

(c) What name is given to the shape formed by this net?

(d) Make an accurate drawing of △ABC.

(e) Use your answer to part (d) to find the height of the shape if it is placed with ACFH as its base.

12 Twenty-seven white cubes are put together to form the cube illustrated in the diagram. The outside of this large cube is pained red.
Three holes are now made through the cube by beginning at each
cube marked X and removing all the cubes through to the opposite
face.

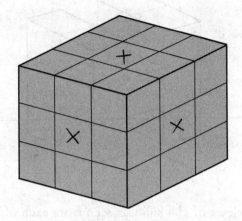

(a)   (i) How many cubes are removed?
     (ii) How many of these cubes have no face painted red?
    (iii) How many of these cubes have exactly one face painted
        red?

(b) For the solid that remains, how many of the cubes have
     (i) exactly one face painted red,
    (ii) exactly four white faces,
   (iii) exactly the same number of red and white faces?

13 Draw the view you see when you look at each solid from the three
directions marked with arrows.

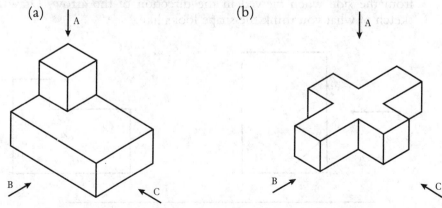

(a) A   (b) A

B   C   B   C

14 The sketch shows a solid with a uniform vertical cross-section, made from small cubes, each with an edge of 1 cm.

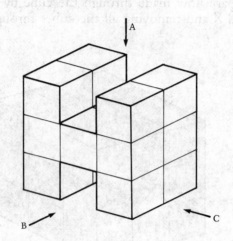

(a) Draw views of the solid as seen from each of the directions A, B and C.

(b) For the solid find
   (i) the number of cubes used,   (ii) the total surface area,
   (iii) the total length of all the edges.

(c) The cubes were originally white, but after they were stuck together, the solid was painted blue. How many cubes have
   (i) 1 blue face,   (ii) 2 blue faces,
   (iii) 3 blue faces,   (iv) 4 blue faces?

(d) Is is possible to reassemble the solid using the same cubes so that no blue faces are visible?

15 The first sketch shows what a particular solid shape looks like when viewed from above. The second sketch shows what it looks like from the side when viewed in the direction of the arrow. Draw a sketch of what you think the shape looks like.

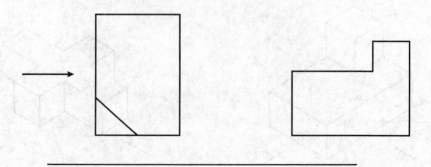

Curved Graphs

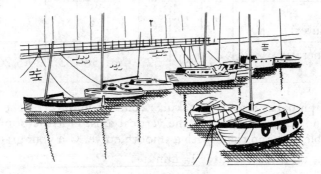

18

1   The depth of water in a harbour at various times is given in the table.

Time (hours a.m.)	0	1	2	3	4	5	6	7	8	9	10	11	12
Depth (metres)	6.8	7.6	8.0	7.7	6.6	4.8	3	1.9	1.5	1.5	2	3	4.2

(a) Plot this data on a graph. Use 2 cm to represent 1 hour on the time-axis and 2 cm to represent 1 metre on the depth-axis. Draw a smooth curve to pass through your points.

(b) Use your graph to answer the following questions.
   (i) What is the depth of water at 9.30 a.m.?
   (ii) A certain ship requires at least 4 metres of water to keep afloat. Between what times is it unable to attempt to dock?

2   The table gives the speed of a Ford Tuna car during road tests.

Time (seconds)	0	5	8	11	16	21.5	28
Speed (m.p.h.)	30	38	47	55	62	55	20

Choose your own scales and draw the graph to show the speed of the car against time.

(a) What is the speed of the car after
   (i) 7 seconds,   (ii) 20 seconds?

(b) How much longer did the car take to accelerate from 30 m.p.h. to 60 m.p.h. than to slow down from 60 m.p.h. to 30 m.p.h.?

(c) What is the maximum speed reached during the test?

3 Water is boiled and left to cool. The temperature of the water at different times is given in the following table.

Time (minutes)	0	1	2	3	4	5	6	7	8	9
Temperature (°C)	100	79	64	52	44	38	33.5	29.5	26.5	24

On graph paper draw axes taking $2\,cm \equiv 1\,minute$ on the horizontal axis and $2\,cm \equiv 10°C$ on the vertical axis. Plot the points given in the table and join them with a smooth curve. Use your graph to find

(a) the temperature after $1\frac{1}{2}$ minutes,

(b) the time taken to cool to 50°C,

(c) how long the water takes to cool from 70°C to 40°C.

4 A stone is thrown vertically upwards from the edge of a cliff. The table shows the distance (s metres) the stone is above the point of projection for various times (t seconds) from the time it is thrown.

Time (t) seconds	0	1	2	3	4	5	6
Distance (s) metres	0	13	16	9	−8	−35	−72

Using $2\,cm \equiv 1\,second$ on the horizontal t-axis and $2\,cm \equiv 10$ metres on the vertical s-axis draw a graph to represent this data and from it find

(a) the time taken for the stone to return to its starting point,

(b) how far it is below the top of the cliff after $4\frac{1}{2}$ seconds,

(c) the time taken for the stone to reach the water which is 80 metres below the top of the cliff.

5 A pottery manufactures jugs with varying capacities but always of the same shape. The table gives the capacity (C litres) for given heights (H cm).

Height of jug (H) centimetres	4	6	8	10	12	14	16	18
Capacity (C) litres	0.06	0.2	0.5	1	1.7	2.7	4.1	5.8

Draw a graph to represent this data taking 1 cm as 1 unit for H and 4 cm as 1 unit for C. From your graph find

(a) the height of a jug which will hold 3 litres,

(b) the capacity of a jug which is 13 cm high.

6   (a) Copy and complete the following table which gives values of x^2 for values of x in the range -4 to 4.

x	-4	-3	-2	-1	0	1	2	3	4
x^2	16	9	4	1	0				

   (b) Draw the graph of $y = x^2$ for values of x from -4 to 4. Use 2 cm to represent 1 unit on the x-axis and 6 cm to represent 5 units on the y-axis.

   (c) Use your graph to find
      (i) the square of 1.7,   (ii) the square roots of 11.

7   (a) Copy and complete the table which gives values of $-2x^2$ for values of x in the range -6 to 6.

x	-6	-5	-4	-3	-2	-1	0	1	2	3	4	5	6
$-2x^2$													

   (b) Draw the graph of $y = -2x^2$ for values of x from -6 to 6. Use 1 cm to represent 1 unit on the x-axis and 1 cm to represent 5 units on the y-axis.

   (c) Draw, on the same axes, the graph of $2x + y + 10 = 0$. Write down the coordinates of the points where the two graphs intersect.

8   Draw axes for x and y for values of x from -4 to 4 and for values of y from -12 to 12. Take 2 cm to represent 1 unit on the x-axis and 1 cm to represent 1 unit on the y-axis.

Plot the points $(0, -4)$, $(1, -3)$, $(2, 0)$, $(3, 5)$ and $(4, 12)$, and draw a smooth curve to pass through these points. These points lie on the curve whose equation is $y = x^2 - 4$. Use symmetry to complete the graph of $y = x^2 - 4$ for values of x from -4 to 4.

On the same axes draw the graph of $y = 4 - x^2$ which is a reflection of the graph of $y = x^2 - 4$ in the x-axis.

Write down the values of x at the points where the two graphs intersect.

97

9 (a) Write down the three values missing from the table, which gives values of $\frac{8}{x}$, where appropriate correct to two decimal places, for values of x in the range 1 to 8.

x	1	1.5	2	3	4	5	6	7	8
$\frac{8}{x}$	8	5.33		2.67		1.60		1.14	1

(b) Hence draw the graph of $y = \frac{8}{x}$ for values of x from 1 to 8. Scale each axis from 0 to 8 and take 2 cm to represent 1 unit.

(c) On the same axes draw the graph of $x + y = 8$. Write down the values of x at the points where this line cuts the graph of $y = \frac{8}{x}$.

10

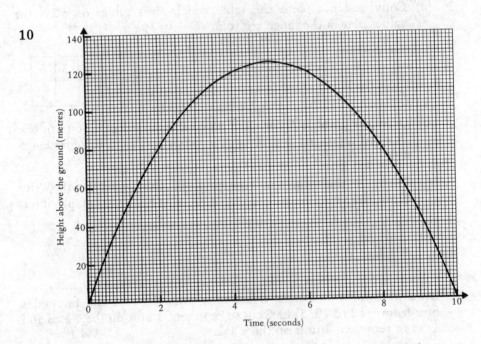

Time (seconds)

The graph shows the height of a stone above the ground during its flight. Use your graph to find
(a) how long the stone was in the air,
(b) the maximum height reached by the stone,
(c) the height of the stone after
   (i) 1.5 s   (ii) 7.7 s.
(d) the times at which the stone was 90 metres above the ground,
(e) the time at which the stone was exactly
   (i) half-way up,   (ii) half-way down.

11 The following table shows how the area of a rectangle increases as its length and breadth increase in the same ratio.

Length of rectangle (L cm)	0	1	2	3	4	5	6	7	8
Area (A cm²)	0	1.5	6	13.5	24	37.5	54	73.5	96

Draw a graph to represent this data using 2 cm to represent 1 unit on the L-axis and 2 cm to represent 10 units on the A-axis. Use your graph to estimate
(a) the area of a rectangle which is
     (i) 5.5 cm long   (ii) 6.7 cm long.
(b) the length of a rectangle which has an area of
     (i) 40 cm²   (ii) 80 cm².

12 Complete the following table which shows the value of the exterior angle ($y°$) of a regular polygon with x sides.

Number of sides (x)	3	4	6	8	10	12	15
Exterior angle ($y°$)	120°		60°			30°	

Draw a graph to illustrate this data using 1 cm to represent 1 unit on the x-axis and 1 cm to represent 10° on the y-axis. Join the points on your graph with a smooth curve.
(a) Use your graph to estimate the exterior angle for a regular polygon with (i) 5 sides,   (ii) 13 sides.
(b) The exterior angle of a regular polygon is 40°. Use your graph to determine how many sides the polygon has.

13 Given below are four equations followed by four sketches. Match each equation with what you think is a suitable graph. The equations are

(a) $y = -x^2$

(b) $y = \dfrac{12}{x}$

(c) $y = x^2 - 4x$

(d) $y = x^2 + 4.$

A

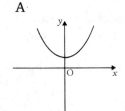

B

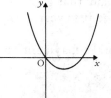

C

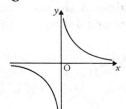

D

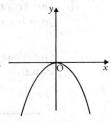

14 In this question several possible answers are given. Write down the letter that corresponds to the correct answer.

The graph of $y = x(4 - x^2)$ could be

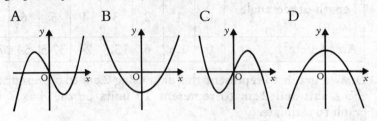

A   B   C   D

15

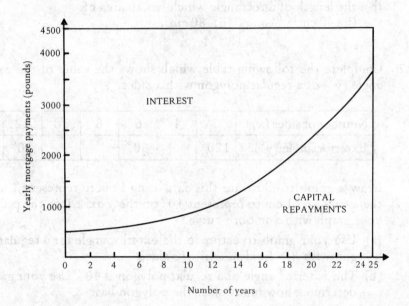

The graph shows the approximate relationship between the interest paid and the capital repayment on a £40 000 mortgage, which is being repaid over 25 years on the assumption of a constant annual rate of interest of $14\frac{1}{2}\%$. Use the graph to estimate

(a) the total cost of the mortgage over 25 years,

(b) the fraction of the total paid that goes to reducing the capital sum borrowed during (i) the first year, (ii) the twelfth year,

(c) the year in which the capital repayment and interest are about equal.

Trigonometry

19

1 Find
   (a) $10 \sin 40°$ (b) $15 \cos 56°$
   (c) $25 \tan 62°$ (d) $14 \cos 16.3°$
   (e) $24 \tan 29.8°$ (f) $9 \sin 76.4°$
   (g) $3.5 \tan 34.9°$ (h) $4.9 \cos 28.5°$

2 Find x if
   (a) $\sin 42° = \dfrac{x}{16}$ (b) $\tan 37° = \dfrac{x}{48}$

   (c) $\cos 73° = \dfrac{x}{32}$ (d) $\cos 64.3° = \dfrac{x}{24.3}$

   (e) $\sin 32.4° = \dfrac{x}{58.1}$ (f) $\tan 44.5° = \dfrac{x}{18.9}$

3

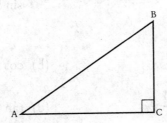

Use the diagram to find BC if
(a) $\widehat{A} = 42°$, AB = 16 cm   (b) $\widehat{A} = 63°$, AC = 29 cm
(c) $\widehat{A} = 73.6°$, AB = 8.7 cm   (d) $\widehat{A} = 70.4°$, AC = 3.9 cm

4

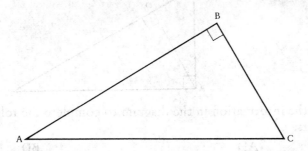

Use the diagram to find BC if
(a) $\widehat{A} = 73°$, AC = 8.5 cm   (b) $\widehat{A} = 59.2°$, AB = 19.2 cm
(c) $\widehat{A} = 34.9°$, AC = 14.7 cm   (d) $\widehat{A} = 26.7°$, AB = 34.2 cm

5

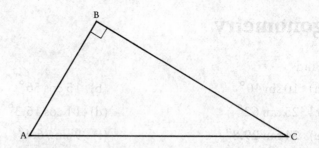

Use the diagram to find AB if

(a) $\widehat{A} = 54.8°$, $AC = 16.3\,cm$ (b) $\widehat{C} = 48.7°$, $BC = 38.5\,cm$

(c) $\widehat{A} = 39.2°$, $AC = 54.6\,cm$ (d) $\widehat{C} = 68.9°$, $AC = 42.2\,cm$

6 Find

(a) $\dfrac{12}{\sin 60°}$ (b) $\dfrac{20}{\cos 43°}$

(c) $\dfrac{15}{\tan 70°}$ (d) $\dfrac{50.4}{\cos 38.2°}$

(e) $\dfrac{37.2}{\tan 22.3°}$ (f) $\dfrac{114}{\sin 51.9°}$

7 Find x if

(a) $\sin 40° = \dfrac{20}{x}$ (b) $\cos 59° = \dfrac{24}{x}$

(c) $\tan 56° = \dfrac{30}{x}$ (d) $\tan 27.8° = \dfrac{42}{x}$

(e) $\sin 21.2° = \dfrac{83}{x}$ (f) $\cos 14.7° = \dfrac{124}{x}$

8

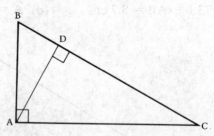

Use the information in the diagram to complete the following statements.

(a) $\tan C = \dfrac{AD}{} = \dfrac{}{AC}$ (b) $\cos B = \dfrac{BD}{} = \dfrac{}{BA}$

(c) $\sin B = \dfrac{AD}{} = \dfrac{}{BC}$ (d) $\sin C = \dfrac{}{AC} = \dfrac{AB}{}$

9

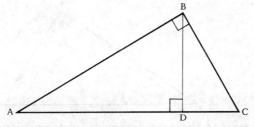

Use the information in the diagram to complete the following statements.

(a) $\sin A = \dfrac{BD}{}$

(b) $\cos A = \dfrac{}{AC}$

(c) $\tan C = \dfrac{BD}{}$

(d) $\sin C = \dfrac{BD}{}$

10

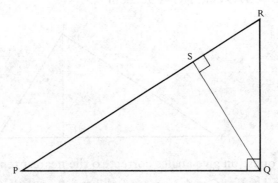

Use the information in the diagram to complete the following statements.

(a) $\tan P = \dfrac{SQ}{} = \dfrac{}{PQ} = \dfrac{SR}{}$

(b) $\cos R = \dfrac{}{RQ} = \dfrac{RQ}{} = \dfrac{SQ}{}$

(c) $\sin P = \dfrac{}{PQ} = \dfrac{RQ}{} = \dfrac{SR}{}$

(d) $\tan R = \dfrac{}{RQ} = \dfrac{SQ}{} = \dfrac{}{SQ}$

11

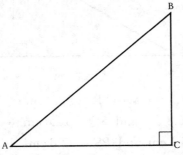

Use the information given in the diagram to find AB if

(a) $\widehat{A} = 43°$, BC $= 14$ cm

(b) $\widehat{B} = 73.2°$, BC $= 18.9$ cm

(c) $\widehat{B} = 23.4°$, BC $= 28.1$ cm

(d) $\widehat{A} = 28.5°$, BC $= 25.6$ cm

12

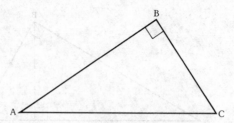

Find $\widehat{A}$, correct to the nearest tenth of a degree, if

(a) BC = 14 cm, AB = 20 cm
(b) AC = 36 cm, BC = 23 cm
(c) AB = 25 cm, AC = 35 cm
(d) BC = 17.8 cm, AB = 30.5 cm
(e) AC = 16.4 cm, BC = 12.6 cm
(f) AB = 37.9 cm, AC = 50.2 cm

13

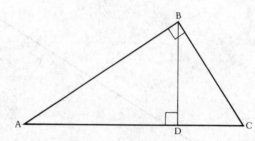

In this question give angles correct to the nearest tenth of a degree.

(a) Find $\widehat{A}$ if BC = 4.2 cm and AB = 6.9 cm.
(b) Find $\widehat{C}$ if BC = 18.9 cm and AB = 24.5 cm.
(c) Find $\widehat{C}$ if DC = 4.29 cm and BD = 5.97 cm.
(d) Find $\widehat{A}$ if BD = 24.7 cm and AD = 18.9 cm.

14

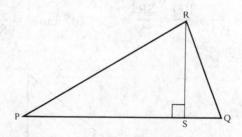

Find

(a) $\widehat{P}$ if RS = 27.3 cm and PR = 38.2 cm
(b) $\widehat{Q}$ if RS = 16.8 cm and SQ = 12.6 cm
(c) $\widehat{P}$ if PR = 35.1 cm and PS = 27.8 cm
(d) $\widehat{Q}$ if RQ = 4.26 cm and RS = 3.97 cm
(e) PS if $\widehat{P}$ = 44° and PR = 15.7 cm
(f) RQ if $\widehat{Q}$ = 62° and SQ = 7.64 cm.

15

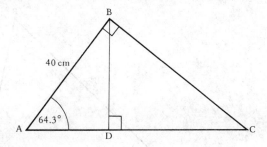

In triangle ABC, D is the foot of the perpendicular from B to AC, BÂC = 64.3°, AB = 40 cm and ABC = 90°. Find BD, AD and BC.

16

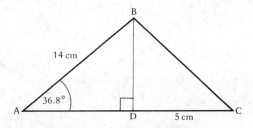

In triangle ABC, D is the foot of the perpendicular from B to AC, BÂC = 36.8°, AB = 14 cm and DC = 5 cm. Find BD, AD and BĈD.

17

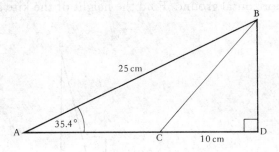

In a triangle ABC, D is the foot of the perpendicular from B to AC produced. If BÂC = 35.4°, AB = 25 cm and CD = 10 cm find BD, AD, AC and BĈD.

18 A vertical flagstaff casts a shadow 25 m long when the altitude of the sun is 38°. Find the height of the flagstaff.

19 A church tower is 40 m high. Find the length of its shadow on level ground when the altitude of the sun is 48.5°.

20

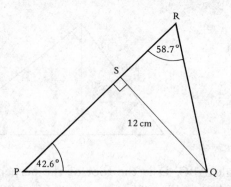

In triangle PQR, S is the foot of the perpendicular from Q to PR, $R\widehat{P}Q = 42.6°$, $P\widehat{R}Q = 58.7°$ and $SQ = 12$ cm. Find PQ, RQ, PS and PR.

21

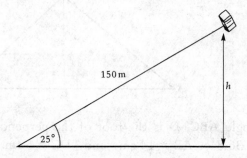

At a particular moment the string that has been let out when flying a box kite is 150 m long and the string makes an angle of 25° with the horizontal ground. Find the height of the kite above the ground.

22

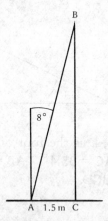

A lamp standard, AB, leans over so that it makes an angle of 8° with the vertical. If C is vertically below B and $AC = 1.5$ m find

(a) the height of B above the ground,
(b) the length of the lamp standard.

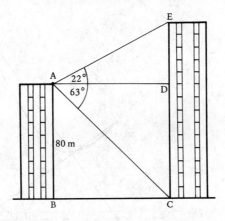

23

Tim stands at A on the top of a block of flats which is 80 m high. He views a nearby block of flats, EDC, and notes that the angle of elevation of the top is 22° and the angle of depression of the base of the block is 63°.

(a) How far apart are the two blocks of flats?

(b) What is the height of the block EDC?

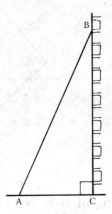

24

A ladder, AB, leans against a vertical wall BC. If the angle between the ladder and the ground is 62° and the foot of the ladder is 5.5 m from the base of the wall find

(a) the length of the ladder,

(b) how far up the wall the ladder reaches.

25

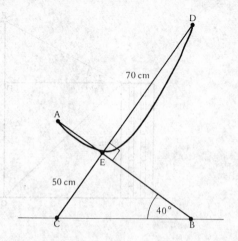

The diagram shows the side view of a garden chair. AB and DC turn about E. A is vertically above C, and D is vertically above B. If CE = 50 cm, ED = 70 cm and ABC = 40° find

(a) AC   (b) AE   (c) DB   (d) BC.

26

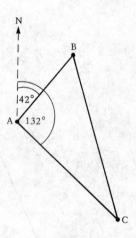

From A the bearing of B is 042° and the bearing of C is 132°. If AB = 4 km and AC = 6.5 km find

(a) B$\widehat{A}$C

(b) A$\widehat{C}$B

(c) the distance of B from C

(d) the bearing of A from B.

108

27

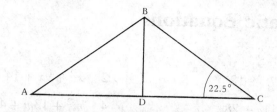

The diagram represents a symmetrical roof truss which is to span a distance of 20 m. Find

(a) the height of B above the level AC,

(b) the length of the sheets (BC) that are required to cover the building.

28

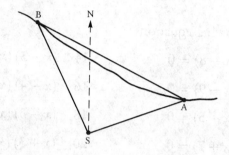

From a ship S the bearings of two points A and B on the coast are respectively 043.2° and 313.2°. If AB = 3.5 km and $\widehat{BAS} = 53°$ find

(a) the distance of S from A,

(b) the distance of S from B,

(c) angle ABS.

29

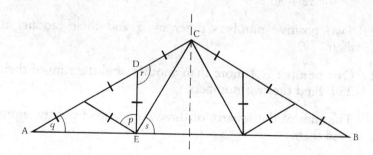

(a) The diagram shows a roof truss that has one axis of symmetry. Find the sizes of the angles marked with the letters p, q, r and s.

(b) If DE = 1 m find
   (i) the span, AB, of the truss,
   (ii) the height of C above the level of AB.

Quadratic Equations

Factorise.

1   $x^2 + 7x + 12$

2   $x^2 + 9x + 14$

3   $a^2 + 11a + 28$

4   $m^2 + 13m + 42$

5   $x^2 + x - 12$

6   $x^2 + 5x - 14$

7   $b^2 - 3b - 28$

8   $x^2 - 7x - 18$

9   $a^2 - 9a + 20$

10   $x^2 - 9x + 14$

11   $x^2 - 15x + 56$

12   $x^2 - 8x + 15$

Solve the following equations.

13   $(x - 2)(x - 8) = 0$

14   $(x - 5)(x - 2) = 0$

15   $(x + 8)(x - 9) = 0$

16   $(x - 4)(x - 7) = 0$

17   $(x + 4)(x - 5) = 0$

18   $(x - 3)(x + 6) = 0$

19   $(x + 4)(x + 7) = 0$

20   $(x + 3)(x + 8) = 0$

21   $x^2 - 11x + 28 = 0$

22   $x^2 - 11x + 30 = 0$

23   $x^2 + 4x - 45 = 0$

24   $x^2 + 12x + 35 = 0$

25   $x^2 - 4x - 21 = 0$

26   $x^2 - 4x + 3 = 0$

27   $x^2 - 12x + 27 = 0$

28   $x^2 + 5x + 6 = 0$

29   $x^2 - 13x + 30 = 0$

30   $x^2 + 6x - 40 = 0$

31   Two positive numbers differ by 5 and their product is 84. Find them.

32   One number is 4 more than another, and the sum of their squares is 250. Find the two numbers.

33   The sum of the squares of three consecutive positive numbers is 77. Find them.

34   The sum of two numbers is 20 and the difference between their squares 120. Find them.

35   The length of a rectangle is 5 cm more than the width. If the area of the rectangle is 104 cm², find its width.

36   The area of a rectangle is 98 cm² and its length is twice its width. Find the lengths of the sides.

37 In a right-angled triangle, the sides forming the right-angle are such that one is 7 cm more than the other. Find the lengths of these sides, given that the length of the hypotenuse is 13 cm.

38 A lawn is 2 m longer than it is wide. It is surrounded by a path 2 m wide which has an area of 168 m². Find the length and breadth of the lawn.

39 The sum of the squares of two consecutive even numbers is 20 more than the square of the next even number. Find them.

40 The side of one square is 5 cm longer than the side of another square. Find the sum of their areas, given that the difference between their areas is 115 cm².

41

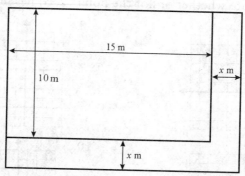

A lawn, measuring 15 m by 10 m, has a path of uniform width x m running along one of the long sides and one of the short sides, as shown in the diagram. If the area of the path is 84 m², form an equation in x and solve it.

Inequalities and Regions   21

1 Solve the inequalities and illustrate the solution on a number line.
(a) $2 + 3x < 5$ (b) $5 > 6 - x$
(c) $9 > 5 + 2x$ (d) $3 < 5 + x$
(e) $3 + 2x > 0$ (f) $2x - 5 \leqslant 7$
(g) $1 + 3x \leqslant 10$ (h) $8 - 5x > 4$

2 Give the largest integer that satisfies
(a) $2x - 3 < 3$ (b) $6 - x \geqslant 2$

Give the smallest integer that satisfies
(c) $2 + 3x \geqslant 8$ (d) $0 < x - 5$

3 Give all the integer values of n that satisfy the inequalities
(a) $2 < n \leqslant 8$ (b) $n \geqslant 5$ and $n < 10$

111

4 Find the range of values of x for which

    (a) $x > 1$ and $x \geqslant 3$ (b) $-1 < 2x + 3 < 7$

    (c) $x - 3 \leqslant 2x < 4$ (d) $11 \geqslant 2x + 7 \geqslant x + 2$

5 Find the range(s) of values of x that satisfy

    (a) $x^2 \geqslant 4$ (b) $x^2 \leqslant 9$ (c) $4x^2 > 25$ (d) $9x^2 < 16$

6 Draw on an xy plane the region that represents $-1 \leqslant x < 4$ and state whether or not the points $(-1, 3)$, $(2, 2)$ and $(4, 2)$ lie in this region.

In questions 7 to 10 give inequalities that define each *unshaded* region. In each case state whether or not the point $(2, 3)$ lies in this region.

7

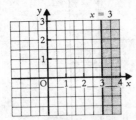

8

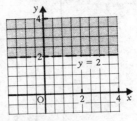

9

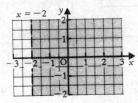

10

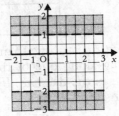

In questions 11 to 14 draw diagrams to represent the regions described by the given sets of inequalities. In each case, draw axes for values of x and y from -4 to 4.

11 $2 \leqslant x \leqslant 3$, $-2 \leqslant y \leqslant 1$ **12** $0 \leqslant x < 3$, $0 \leqslant y \leqslant 2$

13 $-3 < x < 1$, $-2 < y < 3$ **14** $x \geqslant -2$, $-1 \leqslant y < 2$

In questions 15 and 16 give the sets of inequalities that describe the *unshaded* regions.

15

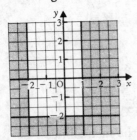

16

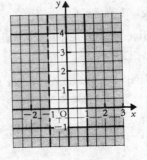

112

In questions 17 and 18, using x and y axes scaled from -5 to 5, leave unshaded the regions defined by the given inequalities.

17 $\quad x + y < 2$ **18** $\quad x - 2y < 4$

In questions 19 and 20 find the inequality that defines the *unshaded* region.

19
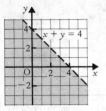

20
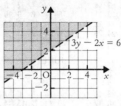

In questions 21 to 26 leave unshaded the regions defined by the given inequalities.

21 $\quad x \leqslant 3, y \leqslant 3, x + y \geqslant 3$ **22** $\quad x \geqslant 0, x - y \geqslant 2, 2x + y \leqslant 4$

23 $\quad x \leqslant 0, y \leqslant 0, x + y \leqslant -3$ **24** $\quad y \geqslant -2, x + y < 4, y < x$

25 $\quad x \leqslant 0, x + y + 3 > 0, y < x + 3$

26 $\quad x + 1 > 0, x + y - 4 \leqslant 0, y \geqslant 1$

27 George is x years old and his brother Hank is y years old. George is twice as old as Hank and the sum of their ages is less than 25 years. Find

    (a) as many relationships as you can for x and y,

    (b) a possible age range for Hank.

Time and Travel 22

Use the calendar overleaf to answer questions 1 to 9.

1 Yesterday it was 17 May. What was the date
    (a) last Thursday,   (b) a week last Tuesday?

2 Tomorrow it will be 26 April.
    (a) What was the date yesterday?
    (b) What will be the date a week tomorrow?

3 Victor leaves on 15 August for a ten-night holiday. On what date does he return?

JANUARY						
M	T	W	T	F	S	S
1	2	3	4	5	6	7
8	9	10	11	12	13	14
15	16	17	18	19	20	21
22	23	24	25	26	27	28
29	30	31				

APRIL						
M	T	W	T	F	S	S
1	2	3	4	5	6	7
8	9	10	11	12	13	14
15	16	17	18	19	20	21
22	23	24	25	26	27	28
29	30					

JULY						
M	T	W	T	F	S	S
1	2	3	4	5	6	7
8	9	10	11	12	13	14
15	16	17	18	19	20	21
22	23	24	25	26	27	28
29	30	31				

OCTOBER						
M	T	W	T	F	S	S
	1	2	3	4	5	6
7	8	9	10	11	12	13
14	15	16	17	18	19	20
21	22	23	24	25	26	27
28	29	30	31			

FEBRUARY						
M	T	W	T	F	S	S
			1	2	3	4
5	6	7	8	9	10	11
12	13	14	15	16	17	18
19	20	21	22	23	24	25
26	27	28	29			

MAY						
M	T	W	T	F	S	S
	1	2	3	4	5	
6	7	8	9	10	11	12
13	14	15	16	17	18	19
20	21	22	23	24	25	26
27	28	29	30	31		

AUGUST						
M	T	W	T	F	S	S
		1	2	3	4	
5	6	7	8	9	10	11
12	13	14	15	16	17	18
19	20	21	22	23	24	25
26	27	28	29	30	31	

NOVEMBER						
M	T	W	T	F	S	S
				1	2	3
4	5	6	7	8	9	10
11	12	13	14	15	16	17
18	19	20	21	22	23	24
25	26	27	28	29	30	

MARCH						
M	T	W	T	F	S	S
				1	2	3
4	5	6	7	8	9	10
11	12	13	14	15	16	17
18	19	20	21	22	23	24
25	26	27	28	29	30	31

JUNE						
M	T	W	T	F	S	S
					1	2
3	4	5	6	7	8	9
10	11	12	13	14	15	16
17	18	19	20	21	22	23
24	25	26	27	28	29	30

SEPTEMBER						
M	T	W	T	F	S	S
						1
2	3	4	5	6	7	8
9	10	11	12	13	14	15
16	17	18	19	20	21	22
23	24	25	26	27	28	29
30						

DECEMBER						
M	T	W	T	F	S	S
						1
2	3	4	5	6	7	8
9	10	11	12	13	14	15
16	17	18	19	20	21	22
23	24	25	26	27	28	29
30	31					

4 Sally goes for a 14-night holiday on 6 July. What date does she return?

5 Robert goes on holiday on 8 June and returns on 21 June. How many nights is he away?

6 Paul goes on holiday on 28 July and returns on 8 August. How many nights is he away?

7 Steve's school closes on 17 July and reopens after the summer holiday on 3 September. How many days summer holiday does George have?

8 John goes for karate lessons every Tuesday lunch time when school is open. The spring terms starts on 3 January and ends on 5 April. School is closed for one week at half-term. How many karate lessons does John get during the spring term?

9 Sara's summer term starts on 9 April and ends on 18 July. Half-term is the week beginning 20 May.

(a) How many Mondays should Sara be in school?

(b) How many days should Sara be in school?

(c) Maths homework is set on a Thursday and collected on the following Tuesday. It is not set over a holiday. How many maths homeworks should Sara get during the term?

10 School starts at 8.45 a.m. and finishes at 3.35 p.m. The lunch break is from 11.45 a.m. to 1.00 p.m.

(a) It takes Sam 20 minutes to walk to school. What is the latest time he can leave home to arrive in school on time?

(b) The first lesson starts at 9.10 a.m. and lasts 70 minutes. At what time does it end?

(c) How long is the lunch break?

(d) How long is morning school?

(e) How long is afternoon school?

(f) Sam takes the same time to walk home as to walk to school. He stays in school for lunch. How long is he away from home during a normal school day?

11 Jen got home from school at twenty to five and looked at the programmes on BBC 1. They are listed below.

3.05	Film: Superman III
5.05	Newsround Review
5.35	Neighbours
6.00	News
6.15	Sports Roundup
6.30	Home Improvement
7.30	Eastenders
8.00	Great Ormond Street
8.30	The Lenny Henry Show
9.00	News
9.30	Billy Connolly
10.20	They Think It's All Over
11.00	Film: Fur And Feather
12.10	Dream On

(a) How much of 'Superman III' had she missed?

(b) How long did she have to wait for 'Neighbours' to start?

(c) How long was the programme 'They Think It's All Over'?

(d) How long was it from the end of 'Eastenders' to the beginning of 'Fur And Feather'?

(e) How much longer is 'Billy Connolly' than 'Eastenders'?

(f) Because of a special news item, Lenny Henry started a little late at 8.36. How long was the special news item?

(g) Lindsey sat down to watch television as 'Great Ormond Street' was finishing, and switched off when 'Fur and Feather' was about to start. For how long did he watch television?

12 One day last summer, sunrise was at 0647 and sunset was at 1926. How long was the Sun up?

13 One day last winter, lighting-up time began at 1623 and ended at 0721 the next day. How long did lighting-up time last that night?

14 The table gives information about a motor racing circuit. It gives the times, in minutes and seconds, taken to complete different numbers of laps for different average speeds.

Average speed in miles per hour (m.p.h.)	Time taken for				
	one lap	two laps	three laps	four laps	five laps
110	2 min 4 s	4 min 8 s	6 min 12 s	8 min 16 s	10 min 20 s
112	2 min 2 s	4 min 4 s	6 min 6 s		10 min 10 s
114	2 min	4 min	6 min	8 min	10 min
116	1 min 58 s	3 min 56 s		7 min 52 s	

(a) How long does it take to do three laps at an average speed of 112 m.p.h.?

(b) How long does it take to do five laps at an average speed of 110 m.p.h.?

(c) How long does it take to do four laps at an average speed of 112 m.p.h.?

(d) How long does it take to do (i) three laps, (ii) five laps, at an average speed of 116 m.p.h.?

(e) How long does it take to do ten laps at an average speed of (i) 112 m.p.h., (ii) 116 m.p.h.?

(f) Estimate the time taken for one lap when the average speed is 118 m.p.h.

(g) Express the time taken for one lap at an average speed of 110 m.p.h. (i) in minutes, (ii) in hours.
(Give each answer correct to three decimal places.)

(h) Use your answer to part (g) (ii) to find, correct to one decimal place, the length of the circuit in miles.

116

Use the information given below to answer questions 15 to 19.

	London	Birmingham	Bristol	Cambridge	Cardiff	Edinburgh	Leeds	Sheffield
Birmingham	111							
Bristol	114	82						
Cambridge	52	100	145					
Cardiff	155	101	44	180				
Edinburgh	378	286	367	338	365			
Leeds	190	111	206	148	212	199		
Sheffield	162	75	163	124	176	235	36	
York	196	134	215	157	242	186	24	56

Distances are in miles.

15 How far is it
(a) from Bristol to York,   (b) from Leeds to Edinburgh?

16 Which city is nearer to Bristol and by how much: Sheffield or Cambridge?

17 Which city is
(a) nearest to London,   (b) furthest from London?

18 Which city is
(a) furthest from Edinburgh   (b) nearest to Leeds?

19 Which two cities are
(a) nearest together,   (b) furthest apart?

20 The time is two thirty in the afternoon. Write this
(a) in a.m./p.m. time,   (b) as shown on a 24-hour clock.

21 A multistorey car park has the following charge tariff:

up to 1 hours	90 p
up to 2 hours	130 p
up to 3 hours	175 p
up to 4 hours	225 p
up to 5 hours	350 p
up to 6 hours	490 p

each additional hour or part thereof 150 p.

How much does it cost to park for

(a) $1\frac{3}{4}$ hours   (b) $3\frac{1}{4}$ hours   (c) 4 hours 12 min   (d) 9 hours?

22 Use this timetable to answer the questions that follow.

		Train times to London					
Button	dep.	—	0924	1042	1142	—	1256
Alford	dep.	—	0935	1052	1152	—	1307
Chipley	dep.	—	—	1105	1205	—	—
Mellow	dep.	—	—	—	1230	—	—
Saxton	dep.	—	1103	1200	1300	—	1410
Sealey	dep.	—	1108	1205	1306	—	1416
Corby	dep.	1125	1130	1238	1330	1442	1438
Stamford	dep.	1139	1143	1252	1343	1439	1452
London	arr.	1318	1323	1431	1522	1618	1637

(a) How much longer does it take to travel to London from Button on the 1042 train than on the 1142?

(b) How many trains stop at Mellow?

(c) What time must I leave Chipley in order to reach London by 4 o'clock in the afternoon?

(d) On which train must I leave Alford to get to Corby by 1320?

(e) How many trains stop at all the stations?

(f) Which train from Chipley makes the least number of stops?

(g) If Alford is 525 km from London, find the average speed of the fastest train from Alford to London.

23 The time on the clock in New York is 5 hours behind the time on the clock in London i.e. local time in London is 5 hours ahead of New York. What time is it

(a) in New York when it is 8 p.m. in London,

(b) in London when it is 3 a.m. in New York?

24 The distance from Bombay to London is approximately 4500 miles. An aeroplane leaves Bombay at 5 a.m. local time and flies to London at an average speed of 500 m.p.h. At what time, local time, will it arrive in London if Bombay time is $5\frac{1}{2}$ hours ahead of London time?

Questions 25 to 27 refer to the following extract which has been taken from a travel brochure.

	Hotel Bali (half board)				Seabank Hotel (full board)			
No. of nights	7	14	7	14	7	14	7	14
Dep. day in week commencing	Sat.		Wed.		Sat.		Wed.	
July 4	225	275	216	251	253	323	245	309
11	233	283	224	259	261	336	252	317
18	244	304	235	270	273	348	264	330
25	256	316	247	282	283	358	274	340
Aug 1	255	325	246	286	281	356	272	337
8	253	323	244	284	279	354	270	334
15	251	321	242	282	277	352	268	332
22	247	317	238	278	266	341	257	320
29	244	304	235	270	259	334	250	312
Sept 5	234	284	225	260	248	321	239	300
12	220	270	211	246	246	319	237	297
19	207	257	198	233	242	306	233	292

Child reductions (2–11 inclusive): 25%.
Deposit: £35 per person; £20 for children 2–11.

25 (a) When is the most expensive time to take a 7-night holiday at the Hotel Bali?

(b) Why do you think it is more expensive to take a holiday that starts on a Saturday than one that starts on a Wednesday?

(c) If I leave on Wednesday 8 September, which hotel offers the cheapest 14-night holiday?

26 How much would a 7-night holiday at the Seabank Hotel, leaving on Saturday 31 July, cost Mr Peacock for a family of five — Mr and Mrs Peacock plus their children aged 7, 12 and 15 years? How much would they have to pay in deposits?

27 The Lawley family, consisting of mother, father and four children aged 5, 8, 10 and 12 years, decided to take a 7-night holiday at the Seabank Hotel leaving on Wednesday 15 September. Find

(a) the deposit,

(b) the total paid to the travel agent if there was a sum, additional to the above, of £10 per person.

When they had been in the resort for a few days they wished that they had booked into the other hotel for 14 nights. How much more would this have cost them? (Include the additional £10 per person.)

119

28 Rob and Cath are planning a holiday in Turkey next summer. An extract from one travel brochure is given below.

Accommodation and Meal Arrangements		SESIN Bed and Breakfast			SUNRISE Bed and Breakfast			PALM BEACH Bed and Breakfast		
Flights Available		All Turkey Dalaman Flights								
Accommodation Code		RIB			RIA			DMY		
Prices Based on		PB WC BL			PB WC BL			PB WC BL		
Number of Nights		7	14	All	7	14	All	7	14	All
Adult/Child		Adult	Adult	1st Child	Adult	Adult	1st Child	Adult	Adult	1st Child
Departures on or Between	30 May - 14 Jun	**275**	**339**	249	**325**	**425**	249	**295**	**372**	249
	15 Jun - 21 Jun	**279**	**352**	269	**331**	**442**	269	**295**	**389**	269
	22 Jun - 05 Jul	**285**	**375**	279	**335**	**462**	279	**301**	**409**	279
	06 Jul - 12 Jul	**299**	**389**	289	**355**	**479**	289	**319**	**425**	289
	13 Jul - 19 Jul	**315**	**399**	329	**369**	**489**	329	**335**	**436**	329
	20 Jul - 07 Aug	**339**	**432**	349	**399**	**526**	349	**365**	**472**	349
	08 Aug - 14 Aug	**332**	**424**	349	**389**	**517**	349	**355**	**464**	349
	15 Aug - 21 Aug	**329**	**415**	349	**385**	**509**	349	**349**	**455**	349
	22 Aug - 28 Aug	**319**	**405**	309	**375**	**499**	319	**339**	**445**	319
	29 Aug - 11 Sep	**319**	**399**	279	**375**	**492**	279	**339**	**439**	279
Supplements per person per Night		Half Board £4.80			Half Board £4.80 Sea View £1.00			Half Board £4.80		

(a) Which hotel gives the cheapest 14-night holiday if they leave on 14 July?

(b) What will they each have to pay if they go for
   (i) a 14-night holiday at the Sunrise Hotel leaving on 10 August,
   (ii) a 7-night holiday at the Palm Beach Hotel leaving on 15 June,
   (iii) a 7-night holiday at the Sesin Hotel leaving on 11 June?

(c) They have a total of £1350 to spend on a holiday, and decide they need £250 of this as spending money. Can they afford to go to the Palm Beach Hotel for 14 nights, leaving on 17 August?

(d) Finally, they choose the Sunrise Hotel for a 14-night holiday leaving on 18 June. They book a room with a sea view and pay extra for half board. In addition they pay £26.50 each for insurance and an extra £23 each to fly from their local airport. How much will they have to pay the travel agent? Have they kept within their budget?

29 (a) If $£1 \equiv \$1.70$, convert £300 into US dollars.
(b) If $£1 \equiv 8.20$ f., convert £115 into French francs.
(c) If $£1 \equiv 178$ pta., convert £46.50 into pesetas.
(d) If $£1 \equiv$ DM 2.48, convert £250 into Deutschmarks.

30 Calculate the rate of exchange if a tourist receives 903 US dollars for £525.

31 Calculate the rate of exchange if a holidaymaker receives 9520 pesetas for £56.

32 A pair of shoes sells for 5940 pesetas in Barcelona. Calculate the equivalent price in Liverpool if $£1 \equiv 165$ pta.

33 Tom Jones buys a Japanese camera in Cannes for 2000 francs. When he arrives home he finds a similar camera on sale in a local shop for £180. If 10f. ≡ 98p, determine whether or not he has made a good buy in Cannes.

34 A British car sells in Belgium for 800 000 f. When the car is sold in the United Kingdom its price is increased by 15%. If £1 ≡ 80f., find the UK price of the car.

35 It costs 40 pesetas to send a postcard home from Spain. If £1 sterling is equivalent to 160 pesetas, find the cost of sending nine postcards home

(a) in pesetas,   (b) in pence.

36 The same English newspaper costs 40p in England but 275 pesetas in Spain. If £1 is equivalent to 180 pesetas, approximately how many newspapers can be bought in England for the price of one newspaper in Spain?

Transformations   23

1 In each diagram, draw the image of the given figure when it is reflected in the dotted line.

(a)

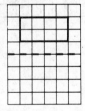

(b)

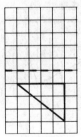

(c)

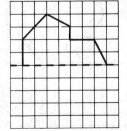

(d)

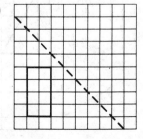

121

(e)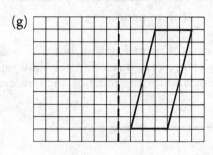

(f)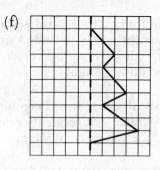

(g)

(h)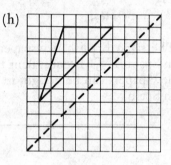

2 In each diagram mark in the mirror line so that the dotted figure is a reflection of the solid figure.

(a)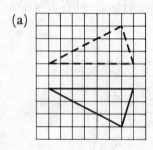

(b)

(c)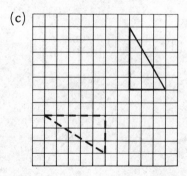

(d)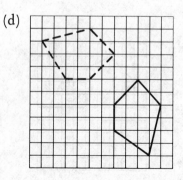

3 In each diagram, draw the image of the given figure when it is rotated through the given angle about the point marked with a cross.

(a)

90° clockwise

(b)

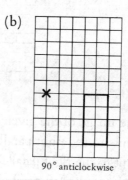

90° anticlockwise

(c)

180°

(d)

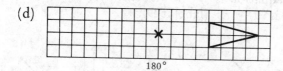

180°

4 In each diagram, the dotted figure is the image of the solid figure under a translation. Describe the translation.

(a)

(b)

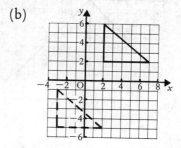

(c)

(d)

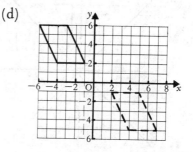

123

5

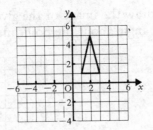

Draw the image of the given triangle under a translation of

(a) 3 units to the right parallel to Ox and 1 unit up parallel to Oy

(b) 1 unit to the right parallel to Ox and 5 units down parallel to Oy

(c) 4 units to the left parallel to Ox and 1 unit up parallel to Oy

(d) 5 units to the left parallel to Ox and 5 units down parallel to Oy.

Label the images I, II, III and IV respectively.

6 In each diagram draw the image of the given figure when it is reflected in (i) the x-axis (label it A), (ii) the y-axis (label it B), (iii) the straight line whose equation is $y = x$ (label it C), (iv) the straight line whose equation is $y = -x$ (label it D).

(a)

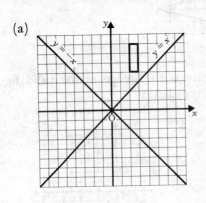

(b)

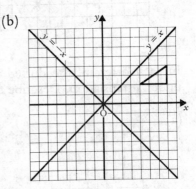

(c)

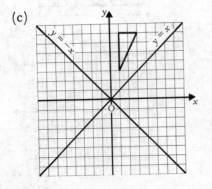

(d)

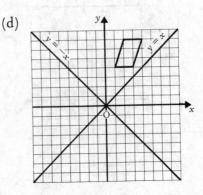

7

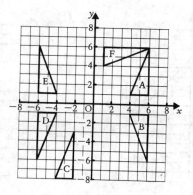

Describe the transformation such that

(a) B is the image of A

(b) C is the image of A

(c) D is the image of A

(d) E is the image of A

(e) F is the image of A.

8 In each diagram the dotted figure is an enlargement of the solid figure. Find the scale factor and the coordinates of the centre of enlargement.

(a)

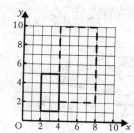

(b)

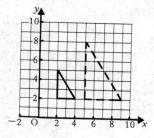

(c)

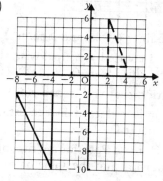

(d)

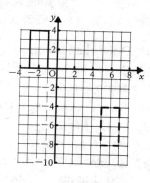

(e) 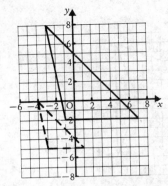   (f)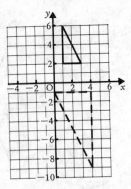

9   In each diagram the solid figure is enlarged using the given scale factor and the point marked with a cross as the centre of enlargement. Draw the image using a dotted line.

(a)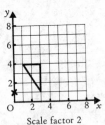

Scale factor 2

(b)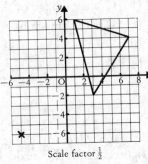

Scale factor $\frac{1}{2}$

10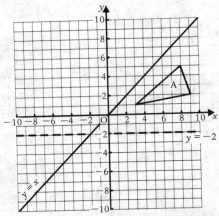

(a) Draw the reflection of A in the line $y = x$ and label it B.

(b) Draw the image of B when it is rotated anticlockwise about the origin through $\frac{1}{2}$ of a turn. Label this image C.

(c) Describe the single transformation that will transform A into C.

(d) Draw the image of C when it is reflected in the straight line whose equation is $y = -2$. Label it D.

(e) A can be transformed into D by a rotation. Write down the coordinates of the centre of rotation and the angle of rotation.

126

11

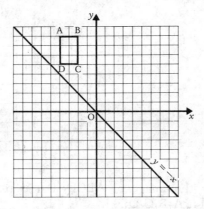

(a) Draw the reflection of the rectangle ABCD in the line $y = -x$ and label it $A_1B_1C_1D_1$.

(b) Draw the reflection of $A_1B_1C_1D_1$ in the x-axis and label it $A_2B_2C_2D_2$.

(c) Draw the rotation of $A_2B_2C_2D_2$ through $\frac{1}{4}$ of a turn anticlockwise about the origin and label it $A_3B_3C_3D_3$.

(d) Describe the single transformation that will transform ABCD into $A_3B_3C_3D_3$.

12

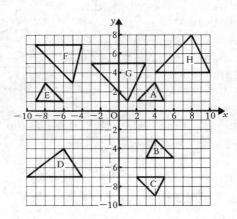

(a) Describe the transformation that maps A onto C.

(b) Describe the transformation that maps A onto E.

(c) Describe the transformation that maps A onto H.

(d) Which of the triangles are congruent with A?

(e) Which of the triangles are similar to A?

(f) Describe the transformation that maps E onto B.

13

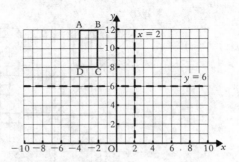

(a) Draw the image of ABCD if it is reflected in the line $x = 2$. Label it $A_1B_1C_1D_1$.

(b) Draw the image of ABCD if it is reflected in the line $y = 6$. Label it $A_2B_2C_2D_2$.

(c) Draw the image of ABCD after it has been rotated through a quarter turn clockwise about the point $(0, 2)$. Label it $A_3B_3C_3D_3$.

14 (a) Write down the coordinates of the vertices of triangle ABC.

(b) B is mapped to B′ by a translation. Describe this translation.

(c) Copy the diagram. If $\triangle ABC$ is mapped to $\triangle A'B'C'$ by the translation described in part (b), mark A′ and C′ on your diagram.

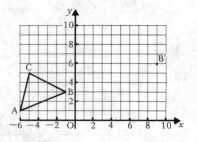

(d) Write down the coordinates of A′, B′ and C′.

15 (a)
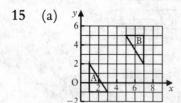
(b)
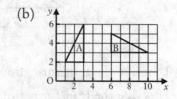

In each diagram, triangle B is the image of triangle A by rotation. Copy the diagram on to squared paper and draw lines that enable you to find the centre of rotation. Write down its coordinates.

Statistics

24

1 The bar chart gives the make of 50 cars in a car park.

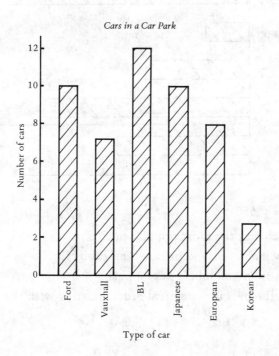

Cars in a Car Park

(a) Which make is (i) most popular, (ii) least popular?

(b) How many are (i) Vauxhalls, (ii) Japanese?

(c) How many are home produced? (Include Ford, Vauxhall and BL in this category.)

(d) How many more were produced in the United Kingdom than abroad?

2

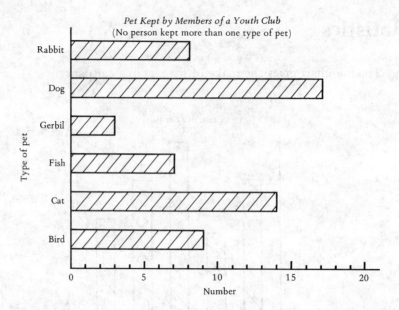

Pet Kept by Members of a Youth Club
(No person kept more than one type of pet)

(a) Which was the most popular pet?

(b) How many more kept cats than rabbits?

(c) How many members kept a pet?

(d) List the pets in numerical order, starting with the most popular.

3

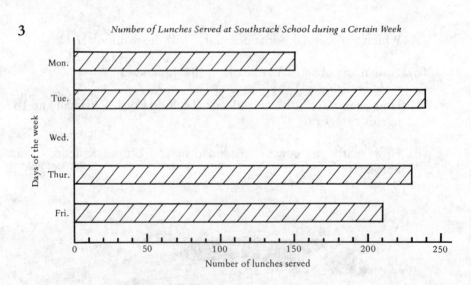

Number of Lunches Served at Southstack School during a Certain Week

(a) On which day were the most lunches served?

(b) How many lunches were served in the week?

(c) What do you think happened on Wednesday?

(d) How many more lunches were served on Thursday than Monday?

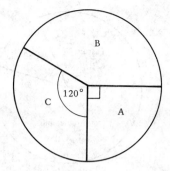

In an election there were three candidates, A, B and C. The number of votes cast for each candidate is represented in the pie chart. A got 1170 votes.

(a) How many votes did B get?

(b) How many more votes did B get than C?

(c) How many people voted?

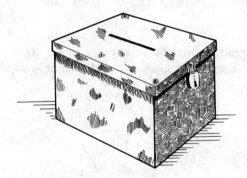

5 The pie chart shows the breakdown of Mrs Hall's bill for £750 from the decorator.

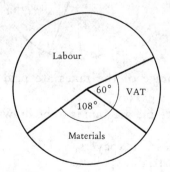

(a) Which fraction of the bill was for labour?

(b) What was the charge for materials?

(c) How much was the value added tax?

(d) How much was the bill before the VAT was added?

(e) What was the rate of VAT charged?

6

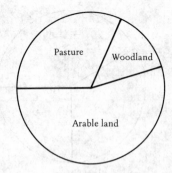

A farm of 1620 hectares consists of pasture, arable land and wood-land as shown in the pie chart, which is not drawn to scale.

(a) If the sector representing the arable land has an angle of 200°, find the area of this land.

(b) The ratio of pasture to woodland is 5:3. Calculate the angle in the sector representing pasture.

(c) How much woodland does the farm have?

7 The pie diagram shows the percentage of the total taxes, collected by a borough council, that are paid by different groups of taxpayers.

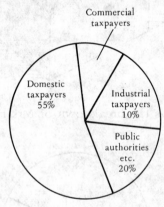

(a) What percentage of the taxes are paid by the commercial tax-payers?

(b) If an accurate pie diagram is to be drawn what is the angle at the centre for
(i) the domestic taxpayers,
(ii) the industrial taxpayers?

(c) Draw an accurate pie diagram for this data.

(d) Give the ratio of the amount paid by domestic taxpayers to the amount paid by industrial taxpayers.

(e) The total taxes collected is £10 080 000.
(i) How much is paid by domestic taxpayers?
(ii) How much is paid by commercial taxpayers?

8   A survey was made of the 360 households in a street. Each household was asked 'Do you have central heating? If so which fuel do you use?' The results are given below.

Fuel	Number of households
Coal	30
Electricity	100
Gas	125
Oil	75

(a) How many households did not have central heating?

(b) Draw a bar chart to illustrate the information given in the table.

(c) For those with central heating what was the ratio of those using oil to those using gas?

(d) What fraction of the whole street had coal central heating?

(e) Draw a pie diagram to illustrate the given information. Include those without central heating.

9   Sue carried out a traffic survey by standing outside the school gates for half an hour one morning. Her results are illustrated by the bar chart.

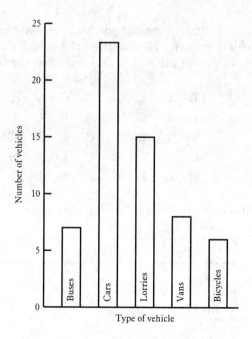

(a) How many cars passed her during her survey?

(b) How many vehicles passed her?

133

10 700 people were asked to complete a questionnaire and to return it within seven days. The graph shows the number returned each day.

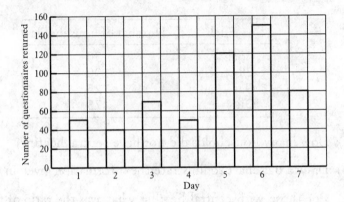

(a) How many questionnaires were returned within the seven days?

(b) How many more were returned during the last three days than during the first three days?

(c) Find, in the simplest form, the ratio of the number who did not return the questionnaire within seven days to those who did.

11 Simon stood on the corner outside his home and noted the different types of vehicle passing. He classified the vehicles as car (C), bus (B), lorry (L), van (V) and other (O), and recorded the following data

$$
\begin{array}{cccccccc}
B & C & L & L & C & C & V & L \\
L & L & C & C & B & B & C & C \\
V & L & L & L & C & C & V & C \\
C & C & L & C & C & L & L & B \\
C & O & B & C & C & C & B & L \\
\end{array}
$$

(a) Copy and complete the following tally chart.

Vehicle	Tally	Total
Car Bus Lorry Van Other		

(b) How many vehicles passed Simon while he was carrying out the survey?

(c) Which type of vehicle was the most popular?

(d) What was the ratio of cars to lorries?

(e) Suggest what the 'other' vehicle could have been?

(f) During the day 4500 vehicles passed Simon's home. Assuming that the types of vehicle were in the same ratio as in his survey,
   (i) how many cars were there,
   (ii) how many buses were there?

(g) Draw a bar chart to represent this data.

(h) Draw a pictograph for this data using one picture to represent three of each type of vehicle.

12 The bar chart illustrates the results of a survey, at the local sub post office, of the number of people using the office each afternoon one week.

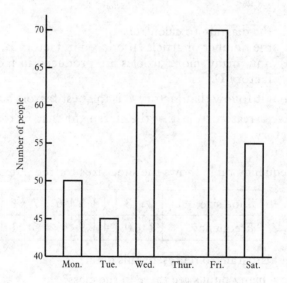

State whether each of the following statements is true, false or not known.

(a) More people used the office on Friday afternoon than on any other afternoon.

(b) 60 people used the office on Wednesday afternoon.

(c) Twice as many people used the office on Friday afternoon as on Saturday afternoon.

(d) 10 more people used the office on Friday afternoon than on Wednesday afternoon.

(e) Thursday was half-day closing.

(f) The range for this set of data is 25.

135

13 The diagram, which is drawn accurately, represents the weekly production of five factories which make the same product. The total number of articles produced is 3750.

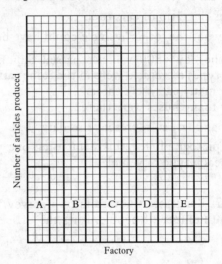

Factory

(a) Use the diagram to calculate
   (i) the number of articles produced in factory B,
   (ii) how many more articles are produced in factory C than in factory D.

(b) Does it follow that factory C is the best factory?

(c) Give a reason to justify the statement that factory E is the best factory.

14 The frequency table shows the shoe sizes for the pupils in a class.

Shoe size	2	3	4	5	6	7	8	9
Frequency	1	0	4	9	6	5	1	2

Draw a histogram to represent this data.

(a) How many pupils are there in the class?

(b) What is the most popular shoe size?

(c) How many pupils take a size 6 or larger?

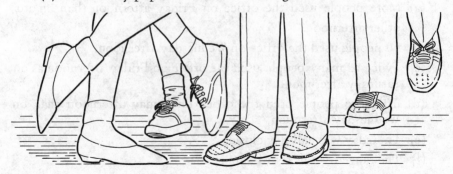

15 The frequency table shows the number of loaves of bread delivered on one day to the houses in Coronation Street.

Number of loaves delivered	0	1	2	3	4	5
Frequency	16	31	14	9	1	2

Draw a histogram to represent this data.
(a) How many houses are there in the street?
(b) How many houses received a delivery of bread?
(c) How many loaves of bread were delivered in Coronation Street?

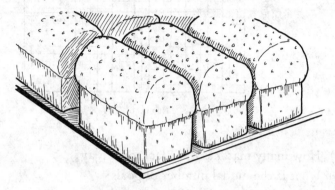

16 The number of words in each line of a page in a novel are given below.

```
11   8 13 10 10   2 10
 9 12 14   8   9   6 11
 9 10 12   8 10   9   9
10   9 12   9   8 12 12
 9 11 12   4 12 10 13
11 10   9   7   2 12   3
```

Draw a histogram to represent this data.
(a) How many lines are there on the page?
(b) How many lines have more than 11 words?
(c) How many words are there on the page?
(d) What is the most likely number of words in a line?
(e) What is the range?

17 Find the mean, median and mode of each of the following sets of numbers.
(a) 20, 16, 11, 16, 14, 27, 22
(b) 29, 28, 32, 29, 30, 34, 29, 29
(c) 71, 75, 73, 86, 74, 70, 85, 70, 71

18 The bar chart shows the number of goals scored by Blacktown FC last season.

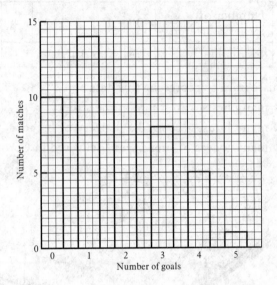

(a) How many matches did Blacktown play?

(b) What is the modal number of goals?

(c) What is the median number of goals?

(d) Find the total number of goals scored.

(e) Calculate the mean number of goals per match.

(f) In how many matches did the team score more than 3 goals?

19 The heights, in centimetres, of seven girls (to the nearest whole number) are 169, 162, 171, 166, 179, 169, 167. Calculate

(a) the mean height,

(b) the median height,

(c) the modal height.

20 Find the mean, median and mode of seven successive rounds for a golfer whose scores were

$$71, \ 84, \ 70, \ 70, \ 85, \ 70, \ 75$$

21 The number of goals scored by a league team in 10 consecutive matches were

$$1, \ 1, \ 4, \ 0, \ 0, \ 2, \ 5, \ 0, \ 2, \ 0$$

Find the mean score, the median score and the modal score.

22 The heights, in centimetres, (to the nearest whole number) of a group of boys are

160, 164, 162, 158, 160, 156, 165, 155, 157, 163

What is
(a) the mean height,
(b) the median height,
(c) the modal height?

23 The hourly rates of pay of five factory workers are

£1.80, £1.65, £1.76, £2.06, £1.73

What is
(a) the median hourly rate,
(b) the mean hourly rate?

24 The hourly rates of pay for a group of workers were

£3.10, £3.65, £2.85, £3.05, £3.10,
£3.43, £3.16, £3.10, £3.10, £3.16.

Find
(a) the mean hourly rate,
(b) the median hourly rate,
(c) the modal hourly rate.

25 The bar chart illustrates the results of a survey into the number of children per household in one street.

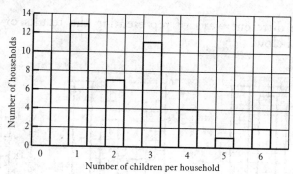

(a) How many households had
     (i) no children,   (ii) 1 child,   (iii) 4 children?
(b) How many households are there in the street?
(c) What is the modal number of children per household?
(d) How many children are there in the street?
(e) What is the mean number of children per household?
(f) A household with one child was replaced by a household with four children. What is the new mean? Redraw the bar chart taking account of this new information.

26 A copy of the Accounts and Report for 1992 for an engineering company gave the following bar chart to show how the operating profit had grown in previous years.

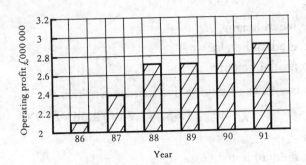

Which of the following statements are true?

(a) Last year there was an increase of £100 000 in the operating profit.

(b) There has been a steady increase in the operating profit since 1986.

(c) The operating profit in 1988 was nearly twice that in 1987.

(d) The operating profit in 1988 increased by the same amount as it had in 1987.

(e) 1987 showed a 300% increase over 1986.

27 Three different ways of representing the results of an election are given below.

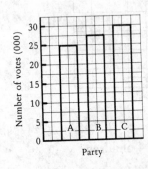 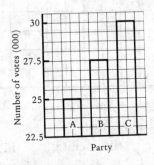 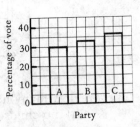

(a) Which method would you wish to see used if you supported
   (i) Party A,   (ii) Party C?

(b) How many more people voted for Party C than Party A?

(c) What was the total number of votes cast?

(d) If 60% of those entitled to vote did not do so, what percentage of the total electorate voted for the party that won?

140

28

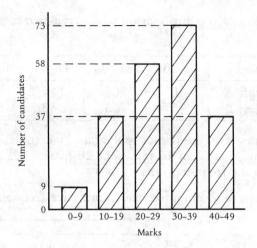

The diagram shows a bar chart to illustrate the marks obtained in an English test by all the pupils entering a comprehensive school.

(a) How many pupils sat the test?

(b) Copy the cumulative frequency table and use the information from the bar chart to complete it.

Marks	< 10	< 20	< 30	< 40	< 50
Cumulative frequency					

(c) How many pupils scored 40 marks or more? What percentage is this of the total intake?

(d) Draw a cumulative frequency curve for this distribution and use it to find the median mark.

29 The results for ten candidates entered for examinations in both history and geography are given in the table.

History	25	37	49	53	57	61	65	77	83	93
Geography	20	40	48	62	54	74	72	84	90	86

(a) Show this information on a scatter diagram. Use $1 \text{ cm} \equiv 10$ marks on both axes.

(b) Calculate the mean mark for each subject.

(c) Draw a line of best fit on your diagram.

(d) A candidate who missed the history examination obtained 54 marks in the geography examination. Estimate the most likely mark this candidate would have obtained in history.

30 The table gives information about the marks scored by 450 pupils in two tests.

Mark	1–20	21–40	41–60	61–80	81–100
Test A	60	165	112	75	38
Test B	15	60	150	127	98

(a) Draw two frequency polygons, one for each test, on the same grid. Use 2 cm to represent 20 marks and 2 cm to represent 20 on the frequency axis.

(b) Copy and complete the cumulative frequency table for each of the tests.

Mark	$\leqslant 20$	$\leqslant 40$	$\leqslant 60$	$\leqslant 80$	$\leqslant 100$
Test A	60	225	337		
Test B	15	75			

Draw, on the same grid, two cumulative frequency polygons, one for each test. Use $2\,cm \equiv 20$ marks and $2\,cm \equiv 50$ on the frequency axis.

(c) Use your diagrams to find, for each test,
   (i) the median score, (ii) the interquartile range.

31 This is a list of the heights, each correct to the nearest centimetre, of 60 children. The list is in numerical order.

```
133 136 138 139 141 143 144 146 147 149 150 151
134 136 138 139 141 143 144 146 147 149 150 152
134 136 138 140 142 144 145 146 148 149 150 152
135 137 139 140 142 144 145 146 148 149 151 154
135 137 139 141 142 144 146 147 149 150 151 154
```

(a) What is the smallest height recorded?

(b) If John's height is recorded as 146 cm, what is the range in which his actual height, h cm, lies?

(c) Copy and complete this frequency table.

Height, h cm	$130.5 \leqslant h < 135.5$	$135.5 \leqslant h < 140.5$	$140.5 \leqslant h < 145.5$	$145.5 \leqslant h < 150.5$	$150.5 \leqslant h < 155.5$
Frequency					

(d) How many children have a height that is less than 145.5 cm?

(e) Explain why it is impossible to obtain from the table the number of children whose heights are more than 148 cm.

Probability

25

1   A card is chosen at random from a pack of 52 playing cards. What is the probability that it is
    (a) a diamond,   (b) not a diamond,
    (c) a three,   (d) a red three,
    (d) the Jack of Clubs,   (e) a black Jack, Queen or King?

2   A letter is chosen at random from the English alphabet. Find the probability that
    (a) the letter is a vowel,
    (b) the letter is a consonant,
    (c) the letter is a, b, c, d, e or f.

3   Gail has a purse full of coins. The table shows the number of each denomination.

Type of coin	1 p	2 p	5 p	10 p	20 p	50 p	£1
Number	12	8	10	6	8	4	2

Andrea selects a coin at random from Gail's purse.
What is the probability that its value is
    (a) 5 p,   (b) more than 5 p,   (c) £1,   (d) less than 50 p?

4   The 'A' Team at Skipton School is made up of 1 boy and 2 girls and the 'B' Team is made up of 1 girl and 2 boys. They agree to play a match. For the first game one player is selected at random from each team. Copy and complete the following possibility space for the different combinations of the two players selected.

		'A' Team		
		B	G	G
'B' Team	G	(G, B)	(G, G)	(G, G)
	B			
	B			

    (a) Use the possibility space to find the probability that the two players who play the first match are
         (i) two boys   (ii) of opposite sexes.
    (b) Construct a possibility space for the different combinations who could play the second match on the assumption that the first match takes place between two boys.
    (c) Use this second possibility space to find the probability that the second match takes place between
         (i) two girls,   (ii) two boys.

5 Copy and complete the table which shows the possible total scores when two dice are thrown.

	1	2	3	4	5	6
1						6
2						7
3						8
4						9
5	6	7	8	9	10	
6					11	

Use your table to answer the following questions.

(a) What is the largest possible score and how many times does it occur? What is the probability of getting the largest possible score?

(b) What is the smallest possible score and how many times does it occur? What is the probability of getting the smallest possible score?

(c) In how many different ways can 8 be scored? What is the probability of scoring 8?

(d) Which score appears most frequently?

(e) What is the probability of throwing a score that is
(i) an even number,   (ii) a prime number?

6 The faces of one cube are marked with the odd numbers from 1 to 11 and the faces of a second cube are marked with the even numbers from 2 to 12. Copy and complete the following table which shows the possible total scores when the two cubes are thrown.

	1	3	5	7	9	11
2						
4	5	7	9	11	13	15
6				13		
8				15		
10				17		
12				19		

Use your table to answer the following questions.

(a) What is the largest possible score and what is the probability of scoring it?

(b) What is the smallest possible score?

(c) What is the probability that the score is an even number?

(d) What is the probability that the score is an odd number?

(e) What is the probability that the score is
(i) 7   (ii) 11   (iii) 13?

7   A book with 260 numbered pages has 13 pages showing pictures. A page number is chosen at random and then turned up. What is the probability that this page

(a) has a picture on it,

(b) does not have a picture on it?

8   A book has 16 numbered pages. Page 1 is a right-hand page, and four of the pages with even page numbers have diagrams on them. David opens the book at random. What is the probability that he can see a diagram on the pages of the open book?

9   Three of the five newsagents near my home regularly stock the *Teenage Times*. What is the probability that

(a) the first newsagent Lesley visits has a copy,

(b) Tom cannot get a copy at either the first or second newsagent he visits? In this case what is the probability that he will get a copy at the next newsagent he visits?

10   Four names are put into a hat: Diana, Eddie, Fred and Greta. Two names are chosen from the hat together. Write down the probability that

(a) two girls are chosen,

(b) one girl and one boy are chosen,

(c) at least one boy is chosen.

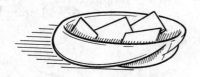

11   What is the probability of throwing

(a) a 6 with one throw of a die,

(b) a 5 followed by a 6 with two successive throws of a die,

(c) an even number followed by an even number with two successive throws of a die?

12   Two dice are thrown together. Calculate the probability that the score is

(a) exactly 12,

(b) exactly 9,

(c) at least 2,

(d) exactly 14.

13 A biscuit tin contains 3 plain biscuits, 4 cream biscuits, 3 shortbread biscuits and 5 chocolate biscuits. When a biscuit is chosen all are equally likely to be picked.

(a) Rita picks a biscuit from a tin. What is the probability that
    (i) she chooses a cream biscuit,
    (ii) she chooses either a shortbread biscuit or a plain biscuit?

(b) After eating the first biscuit she chooses a second biscuit from the tin and eats it. What is the probability that
    (i) she has eaten two plain biscuits,
    (ii) she has not eaten a chocolate biscuit?

14 A bag contains six 50p coins and three £1 coins. Two coins are selected at random from the bag. Copy and complete the following probability tree.

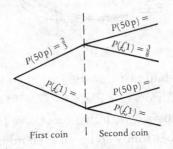

First coin   Second coin

Find the probability that

(a) both coins are 50p coins,

(b) both coins are £1 coins,

(c) the first is a £1 coin and the second is a 50p coin,

(d) there is exactly one £1 coin.

146

15 The probability, $P(E)$, that a girl chosen at random from a class is good at English is $\frac{3}{5}$. What is the probability, $P(NE)$, that she is not good at English?

(a) Complete the following probability tree to show the possible outcomes if two girls are selected at random from the class.

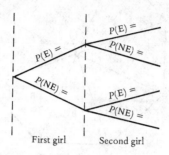

First girl   Second girl

(b) What is the probability that
  (i) both girls are not good at English,
  (ii) the first girl is good at English but the second one is not,
  (iii) just one of the two girls is good at English?

16 A box of chocolates contains 10 chocolates with hard centres and 15 chocolates with soft centres. Paul picks a chocolate at random, eats it, and then picks a second one which he also eats.

(a) Copy the following tree diagram and write the various probabilities on each branch of the diagram.

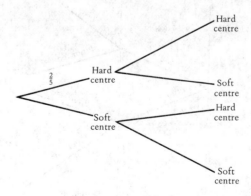

(b) Use your diagram to find the probability that
  (i) both chocolates have soft centres,
  (ii) one of each kind has been eaten.

17 A spinner used in a game of chance has eight possible outcomes, five are red, two are blue and one is white.

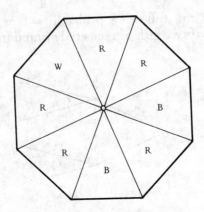

(a) For one turn of the spinner
   (i) what is the chance that the outcome is red,
   (ii) what is the chance that the outcome is blue,
   (iii) what is the chance that the outcome is neither red nor white?

(b) In 80 spins how many blue outcomes would you expect?

(c) In 200 spins about how many white outcomes would you expect?

(d) Copy and complete the following tree diagram to show the probabilities for two turns with the spinner.

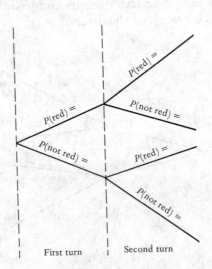

(e) For two turns of the spinner, what is the probability of getting
   (i) both red,   (ii) neither red?

148

18 The times taken by a group of college students to run 100 m are given below.

Time (t seconds)	Frequency
$10 < t \leqslant 11$	2
$11 < t \leqslant 12$	8
$12 < t \leqslant 13$	23
$13 < t \leqslant 14$	27
$14 < t \leqslant 15$	37

Three more students run the 100 m. Their times are 11.2 seconds, 13 seconds and 12.8 seconds.

(a) Draw up a new table to include these times.

(b) How many students have now completed the 100 m?

(c) Using this information, find the probability that the next student whose time for the 100 m is recorded takes longer than 12 seconds.

(d) What is the probability that a student chosen at random took longer than 12 seconds but not more than 14 seconds to run 100 m?

19 Phil buys a bag of bulbs. Three-quarters of the bulbs should produce 'red' tulips and the remainder should produce 'white' tulips.

(a) Two bulbs are selected at random and planted. What is the probability that both bulbs should produce
(i) red tulips,   (ii) white tulips?

(b) The grower states that the probability that a 'red' bulb produces a tulip is $\frac{7}{8}$ and the probability that a 'white' bulb produces a tulip is $\frac{9}{10}$. Copy and complete the tree diagram which shows the possible outcomes when a bulb from the packet is planted.

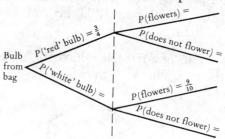

(c) Use your probability tree to calculate the probability that a bulb chosen at random from the packet
(i) produces a white tulip,
(ii) does not produce a tulip.

(d) If the bag contains 320 bulbs how many of these bulbs should
(i) produce red tulips,
(ii) fail to produce a tulip?

(e) If one-quarter of the bulbs had been 'red' and the remainder 'white' could Phil have expected to grow more tulips?

Solving Equations by Trial and Improvement

26

For each question in this exercise find, correct to one decimal place, two positive whole numbers between which the solution of the given equation lies.

1   The length of a side of a square piece of metal is x cm long. The area of the square is given by the equation $x^2 = 30$. (Try $x = 5$ first.)

2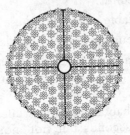

   A circular flower bed has an area of $80 \, \text{m}^2$.
   The radius of the bed is given by the equation $r^2 = \dfrac{80}{\pi}$.

3   The shorter side of a rectangular vegetable garden is x m long and the area of the plot is $70 \, \text{m}^2$. The value of x is given by the equation $x^2 + 4x = 70$.

4   A small rectangular piece of plastic has an area of $17 \, \text{mm}^2$ and is x mm long. It is found that $x^2 - x = 17$.

5   The equation $h^2 + 3h = 67$ arose in a question about a parallelogram. The area of the parallelogram is $93 \, \text{cm}^2$ and the distance between the parallel sides is h cm.

6   The height, h cm, of a triangle which has an area of $50 \, \text{m}^2$ is found by solving the equation $h^2 + 3h = 50$.

7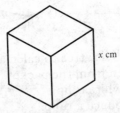

   x cm

   The volume of a metal cube is $70 \, \text{cm}^3$. The length of a side of the cube is x cm. The relation between these quantities is that $x^3 = 70$. (Try $x = 4$ first.)

8   The capacity of a cubical box is $100 \, \text{cm}^3$. The box is x cm deep where $x^3 = 100$.

9

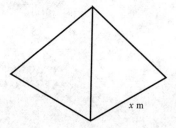

x m

A mound of earth on a building site is in the form of a pyramid with a square base. The total amount of earth in the mound is $180 \, \text{m}^3$. The length of a side of the square base is x m where $x^3 = 540$.

10   The height of a solid is x cm where $x^3 - 7x = 13$. (Try $x = 3$ first.)

Part 2: Revision Papers 1–30

Revision Paper 1

1 (a) Sarah has four coins that have a total value of £1.15. What could the coins be?

(b) Write these numbers in order of size, smallest first.

$$0.444 \quad 0.54 \quad 0.45$$

2 Simplify
(a) $8x + 4x$
(b) $8x - 4x$
(c) $8x \times 4x$
(d) $12x \div (-3x)$

3 (a) I think of a number and double it. I add 5 to the result and my answer is 19. What is the number I thought of?

(b) Solve the equations

(i) $3x + 2 = 4$ (ii) $\frac{x}{3} + 2 = 5$ (iii) $(x - 3)(x - 8) = 0$

4 A coach leaves Birmingham at 0945 to travel to Edinburgh. The journey takes $6\frac{1}{4}$ hours. What time does the coach arrive in Edinburgh?

5

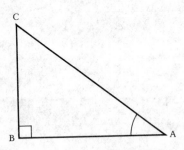

(a) ABC is a triangle in which $A\hat{B}C = 90°$. Referring to angle A state which trigonometric ratios are given by
(i) $\dfrac{CB}{AC}$ (ii) $\dfrac{AB}{AC}$ (iii) $\dfrac{CB}{AB}$.

(b) If $AC = 40\,cm$ and $BC = 20\,cm$ find
(i) angle CAB, (ii) the length of AB.

6 The bearing of the school from the Leisure Centre is 130°. What is the bearing of the Leisure Centre from the school?

7 Find the equation of the straight line with gradient 3 which passes through the point $(3, 4)$.

8   Solve the simultaneous equations

$$3x + y = 17$$
$$7x - y = 23$$

9   Find the angles denoted by the letters a, b, c, d and e.

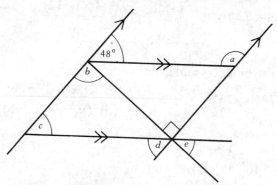

10   (a) For a regular octagon find the size of
         (i) an exterior angle,   (ii) an interior angle.
      (b) Will regular octagons tessellate? Justify your answer.

11   Alan Bates uses his credit card to buy a set of tyres costing £180 for his sports car. For the first repayment he must pay £5 or 5% of the debt, whichever is the greater. Calculate his initial minimum payment.

12   The frequency table below shows the number of goals scored by the home teams in first division matches one Saturday.

Number of goals	0	1	2	3	4	5
Frequency	4	6	4	4	2	1

Draw a histogram to represent this data and hence find
(a) how many matches were played,
(b) how many goals were scored,
(c) how many home teams scored more than one goal.

155

Revision Paper **2**

1. (a) Find (i) $3\frac{1}{5} + 2\frac{3}{8}$ (ii) $5\frac{1}{2} - 2\frac{1}{5}$ (iii) $5\frac{1}{2} \times 2\frac{8}{11}$ (iv) $7\frac{4}{5} \div 1\frac{3}{10}$

   (b) Simplify

   (i) $5a + 7a - 3a + 4a$ (ii) $5a \times 3b$

   (iii) $5 \times (-10)$ (iv) $\dfrac{4 \times (-12)}{6}$

2. Remove the brackets and simplify

   (a) $5(x - 3) - 2(2x + 3)$ (b) $x(x + 3) - 3x$

   (c) $(x + 4)(x - 10)$ (d) $(x - 5)(x + 5)$

3. (a) Give 246.717 correct to
   (i) the nearest 10,
   (ii) three significant figures,
   (iii) one decimal place.

   Give your answer to part (i) in the form $a \times 10^n$.

   (b) Consider the number 503.52. What is the difference in the values of the two 5 digits?

   (c) Given that $1 \text{ km} = \frac{5}{8}$ mile, express
   (i) 260 miles in kilometres,
   (ii) 560 km in miles.

4. (a) Solve these equations

   (i) $5x - 3 = 12$ (ii) $\dfrac{3x + 1}{2} = 8$ (iii) $x^2 = 25$

   (b) If x is a positive whole number calculate
   (i) the values of x which satisfy $5x - 3 < 19$,
   (ii) the maximum value of x if $4x + 3 < 24$,
   (iii) the minimum value of x if $3x + 2 > 20$.

5.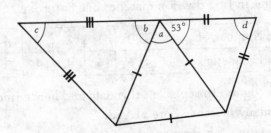

Find the angles denoted by the letters.

6

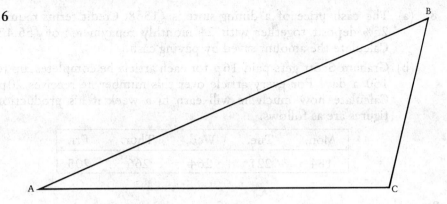

(a) Measure, in millimetres, the lengths of the three sides of this triangle. Hence find its perimeter.

(b) What sort of angle is angle ACB? Use your protractor to measure the three angles in this triangle. Write down the value of their sum.

7

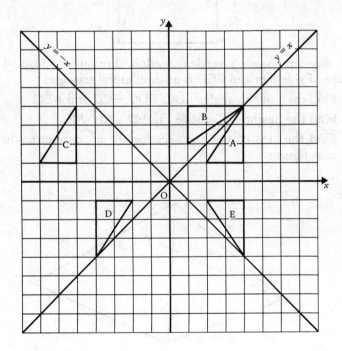

State which single transformation will map

(a) A into B   (b) A into C
(c) E into A   (d) E into D
(e) A into D   (f) B into D.

157

8 (a) The cash price of a dining suite is £1568. Credit terms require 25% deposit together with 24 monthly repayments of £56.40. Calculate the amount saved by paying cash.

(b) Graham Scott gets paid 16p for each article he completes, up to 150 a day. For every article over this number he receives 20p. Calculate how much he will earn in a week if his production figures are as follows.

Mon.	Tue.	Wed.	Thur.	Fri.
184	221	264	266	205

9

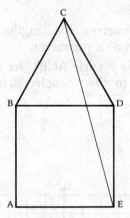

The diagram shows a vertical section through a house. ABDE is a square of side 6 m and BCD is an equilateral triangle.

(a) Find each of the angles $B\hat{D}C$, $E\hat{D}C$, $E\hat{C}D$ and $A\hat{E}C$.

(b) Find the height of C above (i) BD (ii) AE.

(c) Find the area of the cross-section, in m², correct to three significant figures.

10

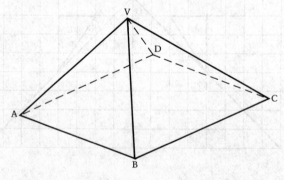

VABCD is a square pyramid with every edge of length 5 cm.

(a) Draw an accurate net for VABCD such that the faces VAB and VBC are joined.

(b) Hence find the shortest distance from A over the ridge VB to C.

158

11 A card is drawn at random from a pack of 52 playing cards. What is the probability that it is

(a) a heart,   (b) not a heart,
(c) a 5,   (d) a red 5,
(e) the 5 of diamonds   (f) a red ace?

12

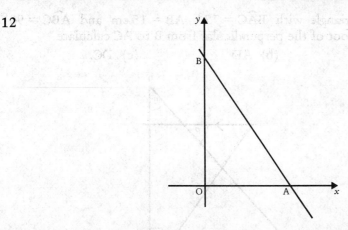

(a) AB is a straight line with a gradient of −2, A being the point (6, 0). Find
(i) the coordinates of B,
(ii) the equation of AB.

(b) AB is now reflected in the y-axis to give the line BC, C being the point where the line cuts the x-axis. Find
(i) the coordinates of C,
(ii) the gradient of BC,
(iii) the equation of BC.

Revision Paper   3

1 (a) I think of a number, double it and add three. If the answer is 17 what number did I think of?

(b) Find   (i) $1 - 7.2 \times 10^{-3}$ (ii) $10\,000 + 2.73 \times 10^5$.
Give each answer in standard form.

2 A lorry arrives in London at 1808 after a $5\frac{1}{2}$ hour journey from Derby. What time did it leave Derby?

3

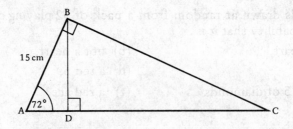

ABC is a triangle with $B\widehat{A}C = 72°$, $AB = 15$ cm and $A\widehat{B}C = 90°$. If D is the foot of the perpendicular from B to AC calculate

(a) BD   (b) AD   (c) DC.

4

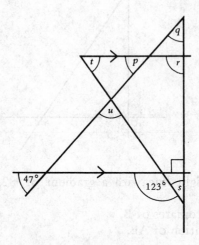

Find the angles denoted by the letters p, q, r, s, t and u.

5   Andrea left home at 7.30 a.m. to travel to the airport which was 126 miles away. She travelled the first 26 miles at an average speed of 52 m.p.h. and the remaining distance at an average speed of 40 m.p.h. What time did she arrive, assuming that there were no rest breaks? What was her average speed for the whole journey?

6   The instructions for cooking poultry are 35 minutes per lb plus 35 minutes.

(a) How long would it take to cook
     (i) a 6 lb chicken,   (ii) a 15 lb turkey?

(b) A turkey took 6 hours 25 minutes to cook. How much did it weigh?

(c) Find a formula to find the time taken, T minutes, to cook a chicken weighing P lb.

7   Find the value of $a^2 + 4bc$ if

(a) $a = 1$, $b = 2$, $c = -3$ (b) $a = 3$, $b = 0$, $c = 4$

(c) $a = -2$, $b = 1$, $c = 2$.   (d) $a = -9$, $b = 4$, $c = -5$

8 Solve the equations

(a) $3(x - 2) - (x + 4) = 1$

(b) $\dfrac{x}{2} - 3 = 0$

(c) $\dfrac{1}{2}(x + 3) = 7$

(d) $\dfrac{x - 3}{2} = 2$

(e) $(x - 2)(x - 9) = 0$

(f) $(x + 4)(x - 7) = 0$

9

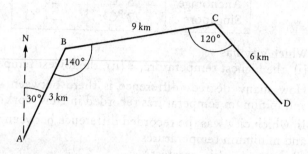

(a) What is the bearing of
(i) B from A,   (ii) C from B,   (iii) B from C?

(b) Make a scale drawing using 2 cm to represent 1 km. Hence find the distance and bearing of D from A.

10

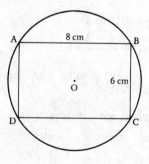

ABCD is a rectangle inscribed in a circle, centre O. If AB = 8 cm and BC = 6 cm calculate the radius of the circle.

11 The benefits of a pension scheme are a lump sum payment equal to $\dfrac{X}{20}$ of the annual salary, together with an annual pension equal to $\dfrac{X}{60}$ of the annual salary, where X is the number of years the employee has belonged to the scheme. Paul Drake has paid into the scheme for 35 years and retires on an annual salary of £21 960. Calculate

(a) his lump sum payment,
(b) his annual pension.

161

12 The table shows the maximum and minimum temperatures recorded one year in five different cities.

City	Temperature	
	Maximum	Minimum
London	28 °C	−4 °C
New York	30 °C	−12 °C
Warsaw	25 °C	−10 °C
Anchorage	15 °C	−26 °C
Singapore	27 °C	24 °C

(a) Which city has
    (i) the highest temperature,   (ii) the lowest temperature?

(b) How many degrees difference is there between the maximum and minimum temperatures recorded in New York?

(c) In which city was the recorded difference between the maximum and minimum temperatures
    (i) least,   (ii) greatest?

Revision Paper   4

1 Solve the following equations.

   (a) $5x - 1 = 24$ (b) $\dfrac{x - 3}{5} = 2$ (c) $7x - 2 = 3x + 22$

   (d) $2(3x - 1) = 7$ (e) $(x + 7)(x + 9) = 0$ (f) $(x + 3)(2x - 3) = 0$

2 Find the angles marked with letters.
   (a)   (b)

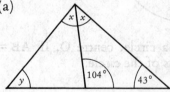
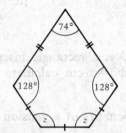

3 (a) My lounge is 4 m long correct to the nearest metre. If its actual length is l m complete the following inequality.

$$\leqslant l <$$

   (b) If $a = 5 \times 10^2$ and $b = 2 \times 10^3$ find (i) ab (ii) $a + b$.

   (c) If $p = 3 \times 10^3$ and $q = 6 \times 10^{-2}$ find (i) $3pq$ (ii) $\dfrac{p}{q}$ (iii) pq^2.

4 Spanish wine is sold in Madrid at 250 pesetas a bottle. Find the equivalent price in London if 100 pesetas ≡ 54p.

5 Diane Eastman uses her credit card to buy an article costing £43.14. For her first payment at the end of the month she must pay at least £5 or 5% of her debt, whichever is the greater. Calculate her minimum repayment.

6 An aeroplane travels at 1296 km per hour.
 (a) How far, in kilometres, does it travel in
   (i) 15 min   (ii) 1 min?

 (b) How far, in metres, does it travel in
   (i) 1 min   (ii) 15 seconds?

7 (a) Divide £7.75 in the ratio 2:3.

 (b) Increase £180 in the ratio 4:5.

 (c) Decrease 36 kg in the ratio 9:4.

 (d) Divide 225 kg in the ratio 5:2:8.

8

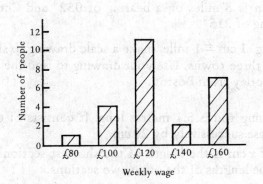

The above bar chart shows the weekly wage of a group of people.
 (a) State the most common weekly wage.

 (b) Find the total number of people in the group.

 (c) Find the total amount received in weekly wages.

 (d) Find the mean weekly wage.

9 Factorise
 (a) $\pi r^2 + 2\pi rh$ (b) $3ab - 12bc$ (c) $8x^2 - 12x$
 (d) $2\pi r^3 + 4\pi r^2 h$ (e) $x^2 - 16$ (f) $x^2 + 4x - 21$

163

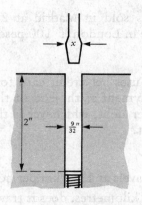

10

Jeff wants a screwdriver to remove a screw 2″ below the surface of a piece of machinery. The cylindrical channel, which gives access to the screw, has a diameter of $\frac{9}{32}$″ and he feels it necessary to use a screwdriver that gives at least $\frac{1}{32}$″ clearance all round. He has a set of screwdrivers, all of which are long enough to reach the head of the screw, with the following diameters:

$$\frac{1}{4}'', \quad \frac{3}{16}'', \quad \frac{5}{32}'', \quad \frac{1}{8}''$$

Which one should he select?

11 Alton, Boston and Chorley are three towns on a map. From Alton, Boston is 8 miles on a bearing of 052° and Chorley is 4 miles on a bearing of 215°.

Taking $1\,\text{cm} \equiv 1\,\text{mile}$ make a scale drawing to show the positions of these three towns. Use your drawing to find the distance and bearing of Chorley from Boston.

12 A fishing rod is 5.1 metres long. It consists of three sections which decrease successively by 20 cm.

(a) If x cm is the length of the shortest section find, in terms of x, the lengths of the other two sections.

(b) Form an equation in x and solve it to find the length of each section.

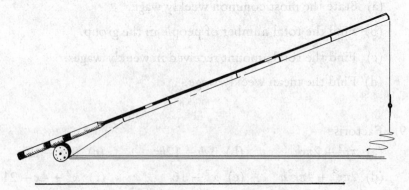

Revision Paper

1 The first six numbers in a pattern are 5, 9, 17, 29, 45, 65.
   (a) Which of these numbers are
      (i) prime numbers, (ii) multiples of 3?
   (b) Write down, in order, the differences between adjacent numbers.
   (c) Hence write down the next two numbers in the pattern.

2 Factorise
   (a) $3x^2 + 6xy$ (b) $x^2 - 6x$ (c) $6x^2 + 3$
   (d) $6x + x^2$ (e) $x^2 - 8x + 15$ (f) $x^2 - x - 20$

3 If $a = 2.4 \times 10^4$ and $b = 5 \times 10^{-2}$ find

   (a) ab (b) $\dfrac{a}{b}$.

   Give each answer in standard form.

4 Sally has six coins in her purse. They have a total value of 58 p. What could the coins be?

5 Peter, who is 1.8 m tall, stands 28 m from the foot of a vertical building and finds that the angle of elevation of the top of the building is 60°. How high is the building?

6 An ice-cream seller receives a basic wage of £50 per week plus commission at 15% on weekly sales over £60. Calculate his wage in a week when his takings amount to £880.

7 (a) If $v^2 = u^2 + 2as$ find s in terms of v, u and a.
   (b) Find the value of s when
      (i) $v = 8$, $u = 6$ and $a = 7$.
      (ii) $v = 5$, $u = 11$ and $a = -8$.

8 Given below is a set of marks obtained by 20 pupils in a history test.

4	13	30	37	1
23	10	45	42	9
10	17	4	10	8
32	13	46	26	40

   (a) Find
      (i) the range,
      (ii) the mode,
      (iii) the arithmetic mean of these marks.
   (b) If the maximum possible score is 50, what percentage of the group scored more than half marks?

9   The diagram shows a washer with an outer radius of R cm and an inner radius of r cm.

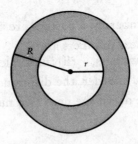

Show that the area of the shaded region, A cm^2, is given by $A = \pi(R^2 - r^2)$.

Express R^2 in terms of A, r and π. By taking the positive square root of both sides, express R in terms of the other letters.

10 A, B and C represent three towns. B is 4 km north-east of A, and C is 8 km south-east of B. Draw a diagram to show the positions of the three towns and find

(a) the distance,   (b) the direction,   of A from C.

11 Draw axes for x and y. Scale each axis from 0 to 10 using 1 cm as 1 unit on both axes. Plot the points A(2, 4), B(1, 1), C(5, 0), D(9, 3) and E(8, 4). Complete the figure so that it is symmetrical about AE. Find the area of the completed figure.

12 Copy and complete the table which gives the value of $\dfrac{5x^2}{2}$ for values of x from -4 to 4.

x	-4	-3	-2	-1	0	1	2	3	4
$\dfrac{5x^2}{2}$	40	22.5		2.5		2.5			

Hence draw the graph of $y = \dfrac{5x^2}{2}$ using 2 cm for 1 unit on the x-axis and 4 cm for 10 units on the y-axis.

On the same axes draw the graph of $y = 3x + 10$. Write down the values of x at the points of intersection of the two graphs.

Revision Paper 6

1 (a) Deborah earns £224 for working 35 hours. How much does she get paid per hour?

   (b) Ben leaves home at 0750 to drive to Oxford. He arrives in Oxford at 1120. How long did his journey take? If Ben had travelled 140 miles, what was his average speed?

2 Write down the terms represented by question marks in each of the following sequences:

   (a) 2, 5, 10, 17, 26, ?, ?,

   (b) 729, 243, 81, ?, 9, 3, 1, ?, ?,

   (c) 18, 36, 72, ?, 288, ?.

3 (a) Factorise (i) $9x - 18$ (ii) $9x^2 + 3x$ (iii) $2\pi r^2 + \pi rh$.

   (b) Simplify (i) $3(4x + 3) - 2(3x - 7)$ (ii) $(x + 4)(x - 9)$.

4 A photograph measuring 12 cm by 10 cm is to be enlarged such that every linear dimension increases in the ratio 2:3. Find

   (a) the dimensions,   (b) the area,   of the enlargement.

5 Construct a triangle ABC in which AB = 12.4 cm, BC = 9.2 cm and AC = 10.8 cm. Construct the perpendicular bisector of AB to cut the bisector of angle BAC at P. Write down the length of AP.

6

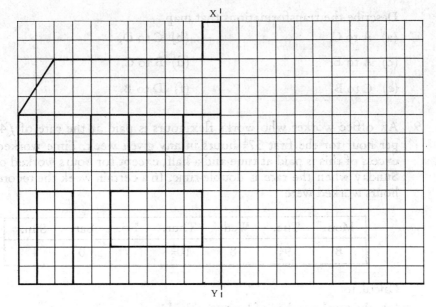

The diagram shows a simplified front view of a semi-detached house. Complete the diagram so that it is symmetrical about XY.

7   Paul bought a motorcycle from a dealer for £990.

(a) If the dealer bought the machine for £720 find his percentage profit.

(b) If Paul shared the cost with his father in the ratio 7 : 4 how much did his father pay?

(c) The value of his motorcycle depreciates each year by 20% of its value at the beginning of that year. What was it worth after two years? Give your answer correct to the nearest £10.

8   In the diagram, A is mapped on to B by a reflection in the x-axis.

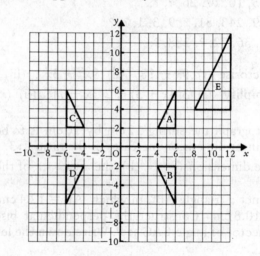

Describe the transformations that map

(a) A to C,   (b) C to D,

(c) A to E,   (d) B to C,

(e) C to B,   (f) D to B.

9   An office worker who works flexihours is paid at the rate of £4.50 per hour for the first $37\frac{1}{2}$ hours in any given week. Time worked in excess of this is paid at time-and-a-half, except for hours worked on a Sunday when the rate is double-time. In a certain week the recorded hours worked were:

Mon.	Tue.	Wed.	Thur.	Fri.	Sat.	Sun.
8	$9\frac{1}{2}$	8	$10\frac{1}{2}$	7	0	4

Calculate

(a) the total number of hours worked in the week,

(b) the gross wage.

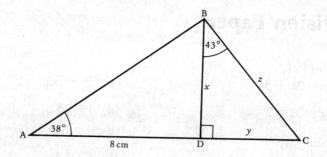

10

Use the information given in the diagram to find the values of x, y and z.

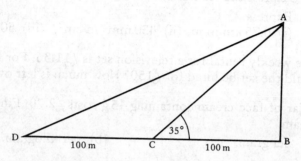

From a boat, C, 100 m from the base, B, of a vertical cliff, AB, the angle of elevation of the top, A, is 35°.

(a) Calculate the height of the cliff, giving your answer correct to the nearest metre.

(b) The boat moves directly away from the cliff a further distance of 100 m to a point D. Calculate the angle of elevation of A from D.

12 A motorist travels 168 miles in $3\frac{1}{2}$ hours.

(a) Calculate his average speed for this journey in m.p.h.

(b) His car will drive 46 miles on each gallon of petrol. What is the least whole number of gallons of petrol he needs to complete the journey?

(c) He starts his journey at 0815. At what time should he arrive?

(d) What is the length of his journey in kilometres? (5 miles ≡ 8 km.)

1 Simplify
 (a) $2\frac{1}{2} + 3\frac{3}{4}$ (b) $5\frac{3}{5} - 3\frac{1}{10}$
 (c) $3\frac{1}{2} \div 2$ (d) $1\frac{2}{3} \times 3$.

2 Simplify
 (a) $5x + 2y - 3x + 4y$ (b) $3a \times 4a$
 (c) $(3a^3)^2$ (d) $\sqrt{4a^2b^2}$.

3 (a) The plan of a house is drawn so that $\frac{1}{2}$ cm represents 1 m. Express the scale as a ratio.
 (b) Express
   (i) 0.75 km in m, (ii) 430 mm² in cm², (iii) 500 000 cm³ in m³.

4 The weekly rental for a television set is £11.36. For how many weeks could the set be hired for £150? How much is left over?

5 A jar of face cream containing 45 g costs £2.70. Find the cost of this cream
 (a) per gram,   (b) per kilogram.

6
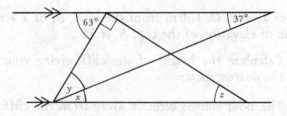
Find the angles marked with letters.

7 Alan lies down on the top of a vertical cliff that he knows to be 60 m high. He observes that the angle of depression of a boat that is directly out to sea is 34.5°. How far is the boat from the base of the cliff?

8
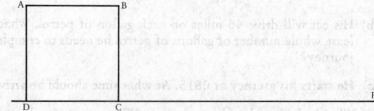

A cube is turned about C until CB rests on the floor. It is then turned about B until BA lies on the floor, and so on until A returns to its original relative position. Sketch the locus of A.

9 Semicircles are drawn on the three sides of a right-angled triangle ABC, in which AB = 8 cm and BC = 6 cm.

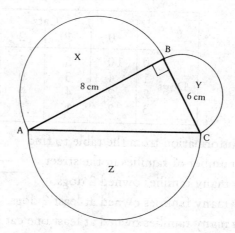

(a) Use Pythagoras' result to find the length of AC.

(b) Write down the radii of each of the three semicircles.

(c) Write down, in terms of π, the area of each of the three semicircles.

(d) What is the relationship between the areas marked X, Y and Z?

(e) If equilateral triangles had been drawn on the three sides instead of semicircles, would your answer to part (d) have been different?

10 Trees are planted on both sides of a straight road which is 1 kilometre long. On one side they are planted at intervals of 20 m but on the other side they are planted at intervals of 25 m. At one end two trees are exactly opposite each other.

(a) At how many places along the road are two trees exactly opposite?

(b) How many trees are there altogether?

11 The cost of running my car for a year is as follows: road tax £135, insurance £365, depreciation £1250, petrol 1950 litres at 60 p per litre, servicing and repairs £175. Calculate

(a) the total cost of the fixed charges, including servicing and repairs,

(b) the total petrol costs for the year,

(c) the total cost of motoring for the year,

(d) the distance I travel if the car averages 12.5 km per litre,

(e) the total average cost per kilometre, giving your answer in pence correct to three significant figures.

Express the petrol costs as a percentage of the total costs, giving your answer correct to the nearest whole number.

12 The table shows the number of cats and dogs owned by the families in a street (e.g. 10 families owned neither a cat nor a dog).

		Cats			
		0	1	2	3
Dogs	0	10	5	3	0
	1	4	3	0	1
	2	2	4	0	0
	3	2	1	1	1

Use the information from the table to find
(a) the number of families in the street,
(b) how many families owned 2 dogs,
(c) how many families owned at least 2 dogs,
(d) how many families owned at least one cat,
(e) how many families owned more than 2 of these pets,
(f) the total number of dogs and cats owned by the families in this street.

Revision Paper   8

1 New cars lose about 20% of their value each year. Arthur paid £16 000 for a new car. What will it be worth when it is one year old?

2 Given that $p = 3$ and $q = -4$ find the value of
(a) $2p + q$ (b) $p^2 + q^2$ (c) $2pq$.

3 Find the value of x in each of the following figures.
(a)
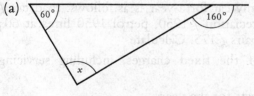

(b)
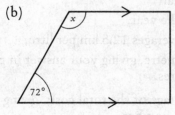

(c)
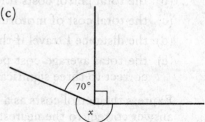

4 (a) Make D the subject of the formulae
　　　(i) $C = \pi D$,　　(ii) $A = \dfrac{\pi D^2}{4}$.

　　　Find an expression for A in terms of C and π.

　(b) If 1 gallon is equivalent to 4.54 litres express
　　　(i) 5 gallons in litres,　　(ii) 50 litres in gallons.

5
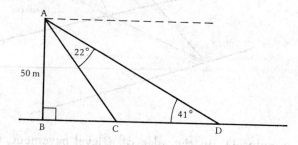

Find
　(a) the angle of elevation of A from C,

　(b) the angle of depression of D from A,

　(c) the length of (i) BD　(ii) BC.

6　Three jobs are advertised in the local newspaper.

　　　A. Trainee in the Architect's Department at County
　　　　　Hall: £9100 per year
　　　B. Nursery Assistant: £700 per calendar month
　　　C. Building Worker: £237.50 per week

　(a) How much will the trainee earn in a week?

　(b) How much will the nursery assistant earn in a year?

　(c) How much will the building worker earn in a year?

　(d) Which job is the best paid?

　(e) Which job has the best prospects?

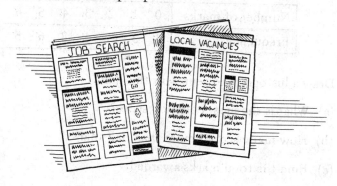

7

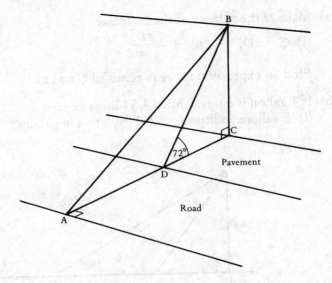

Pavement

Road

(a) A point D, on the edge of a level pavement, is 10 m from the base C of a vertical building BC. If the elevation from D of the top of the building B is 72° find the height of the building.

(b) The road running parallel to the pavement is 9.5 m wide. If A is the point on the opposite side of the road from D and if A, B, C and D lie in the same vertical plane, find the angle of elevation of B from A.

8 Solve the equations
   (a) $(x + 7)(x - 5) = 0$
   (b) $x^2 + 3x - 28 = 0$
   (c) $4x^2 = 9$
   (d) $x^2 - 25 = 0$.

9 The frequency table below shows the number of marks, out of 8, scored in a maths test by the 34 children in a class.

Number of marks	0	1	2	3	4	5	6	7	8
Frequency	1	3	2	4	8	6	5	3	2

Draw a histogram to represent this data.

(a) What is the most common score?

(b) How many scored more than half marks?

(c) Find the total marks awarded.

10   A bag of bulbs will produce spring flowers that are red, blue or white. The probability that a bulb chosen at random will produce a red or blue or white flower is

probability that the flower is red	$\frac{1}{2}$
probability that the flower is blue	$\frac{1}{3}$
probability that the flower is white	p

(a) What is the probability that a bulb chosen at random will give
  (i) a white flower,
  (ii) a flower that is not blue?

(b) Two bulbs are selected at random. What is the probability that when they flower
  (i) both flowers are white,
  (ii) one flower is red and the other blue,
  (iii) both flowers are the same colour,
  (iv) the flowers are different colours?

11

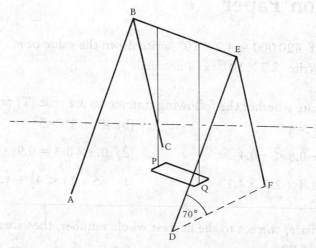

A garden swing is constructed from four equal 3-metre lengths of angle iron resting on level ground as shown in the diagram. They support a horizontal bar, BE, of length 2 m. The seat, PQ, is supported by two chains such that when the seat is in its lowest position, it is 0.5 m above the ground. If the supports each make an angle of 70° with the horizontal calculate

(a) the height of the rod BE above the ground,

(b) the length of each chain,

(c) the area of ground ADFC.

If the seat PQ swings so that at its furthest position from the vertical each chain is parallel to the supports, find

(d) the angle through which the chains supporting the seat move from one extreme to the other,

(e) the maximum height of the seat above the ground.

175

12 The table shows the pension position of Mr and Mrs Average.

	Age at which pension becomes due	Life expectancy	Amount of retirement pension per week
Mr Average	65	67	£69
Mrs Average	60	72	£69

Using this information, calculate how much more in total Mrs Average can expect to receive than Mr Average.

Revision Paper   9

1 (a) If $420\,000 = 4.2 \times 10^n$ write down the value of n.

(b) Write 2.7×10^{-3} as a decimal.

2 Indicate whether the following statements are true (T) or false (F).

(a) $\frac{1}{2} > \frac{1}{3}$ (b) $4^2 + 3^2 > 5^2$

(c) $-0.5 < -0.4$ (d) $0.3 \times 0.3 = 0.9$

(e) $1.4 \times 2.7 > 4.1$ (f) $55 \div 11 < 4\frac{1}{2} + \frac{2}{3}$.

3 Estimate, correct to the nearest whole number, the value of

(a) $\dfrac{35.98}{8.9}$ (b) 5.02^2 (c) $\sqrt{50}$.

4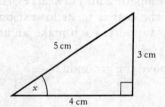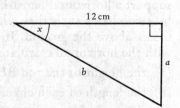

These two triangles are similar. Find the lengths of the sides marked a and b.

5 Which is the cheaper petrol, 54.7 p per litre or £2.51 per gallon? (1 gallon ≡ 4.54 litres.)

6   Five girls collect money for a sponsored walk. The amounts collected are £7, £3, £5, £9, £11. Find the mean (average) amount collected.

7   Bob and Janet Pond pay for their new fitted kitchen costing £5000, using a credit card. Interest at 4% is added at the end of each month. They pay £400 off their debt each month, the day after the interest has been added. How much will they owe *before* they make their third payment?

8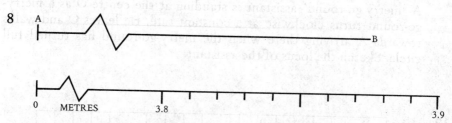

A room is measured using a measuring tape. One end A, corresponds to 0 on the tape. The other end is shown in the diagram. How long is the room?

9   A cylindrical breakfast cup has a radius of 4 cm and is 8 cm high. Find the surface area of the cup in contact with tea when it is filled to within 0.5 cm of the top. Neglect the thickness of the cup.

10 Jack Burley's work-card for a week gave the following 'clocking in' and 'clocking out' times.

	In	Out
Mon	7.30 a.m.	3.30 p.m.
Tues	7.30 a.m.	5.15 p.m.
Wed	7.30 a.m.	3.30 p.m.
Thurs	7.30 a.m.	5.15 p.m.
Fri	8.30 a.m.	3.30 p.m.
Sat	7.30 a.m.	12.30 p.m.

(a) If he works overtime on two days, what is the length of the normal working day?

(b) How many hours of overtime does he work, excluding Saturday morning?

(c) The basic rate of payment is £4.95 per hour, with time-and-a-half for overtime and double-time for Saturday morning. Calculate his gross wage for the week.

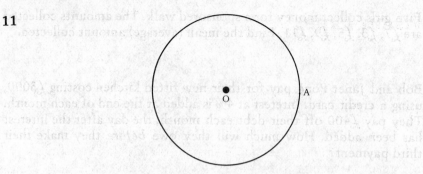

A 'merry-go-round' assistant is standing at the centre O as a merry-go-round turns clockwise at a constant rate. He leaves O and walks towards A arriving there when the merry-go-round has turned full circle. Sketch the locus of the assistant.

12

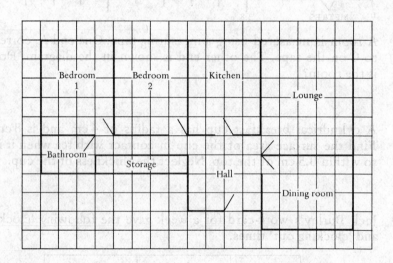

This is the plan of a bungalow. Each square on the grid has a side of $\frac{1}{2}$ cm and represents a length of 1 metre in the bungalow.

Copy and complete the following table.

	Length (m)	Width (m)	Area (m²)
Lounge	6	5	30
Dining Room			
Kitchen			
Hall			
Bathroom			
Bedroom 1			
Bedroom 2			

Revision Paper

10

1   Solve the equations
    (a) $2x - 3 = 5$
    (b) $5x - 7 = 3x + 9$
    (c) $\frac{1}{3}(x + 2) = 4$
    (d) $2x + 4 = 3x - 1$.

2   A thermometer in a greenhouse showed that the lowest temperature recorded one winter night was $-5\,°C$. The highest temperature recorded the following day was $4\,°C$. What is the difference between the highest and lowest temperatures?

3

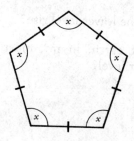

   (a) Write down the name of this figure.
   (b) Find the value of x.
   (c) What is the size of an exterior angle of this figure?
   (d) Will this shape tessellate? Justify your answer.

4   A food mixer may be bought on credit terms by paying a deposit of £14.60 together with 26 equal payment of £2.17. Find the total price if bought on credit. If this is £8.54 more than the cash price, find the cash price.

5

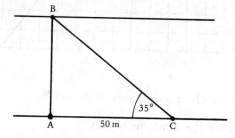

   Janet stands at A on one bank of a river which is directly opposite a tree at B on the opposite bank. She walks 50 m downstream to a point C and finds the line from C to B makes an angle of 35° with the bank. How wide is the river?

6

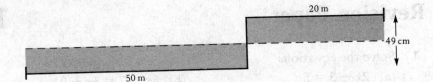

20 m

49 cm

50 m

Norman Cale's garden is on two levels, the higher level being 49 cm above the lower level. The lower level is 50 m long and the higher level is 20 m long. The plot is 20 m wide throughout. He wishes to remove earth from the higher level to build-up the lower level until the whole garden is one flat surface.

(a) What depth of soil must he remove from the higher level?

(b) How much will the lower level rise?

(c) What volume of earth, in m³, must he move from the upper level to the lower level?

7

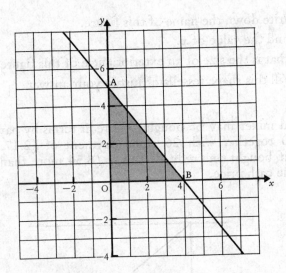

(a) Write down the coordinates of A and B.

(b) Write down the gradient of AB.

(c) If the equation of the straight line AB is $y = mx + c$ use your answers to parts (a) and (b) to write down the value of
(i) m (ii) c.

(d) Use inequalities to define the region that is shaded.

8   Coffee is sold in four different sizes.

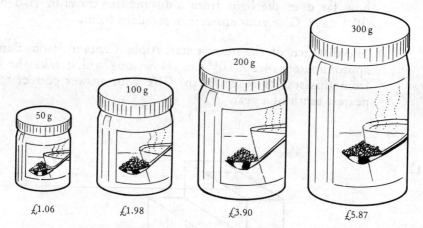

£1.06   £1.98   £3.90   £5.87

(a) How much is saved by buying one 300 g jar rather than
     (i) three 100 g jars,   (ii) six 50 g jars?
(b) Which jar gives the best value for money? Justify your choice.

9

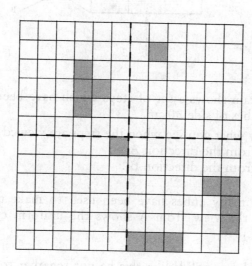

The diagram shows part of the pattern for a crossword puzzle. Copy
and complete the diagram so that it is symmetrical about both the
marked axes.

10 (a) Find the map ratio of a map on which 5 cm represents 1 km.
    (b) The map ratio of a map is 1 : 250 000.
        (i)   The distance between two villages is 15 km. What does this
              measure on the map?
        (ii) On the map, the distance between Tom's home and his
              place of work is 7.5 cm. How far is Tom's workplace from
              his home?

11 (a) If the speed of light is approximately 300 000 km per second, how far does the light from a distant star travel in (i) 1 hour, (ii) 1 day? Give your answers in standard form.

(b) The distance of the nearest star, Alpha Centauri, from Earth is approximately 4.2×10^{13} km. How long will it take the light from this star to reach Earth? Give your answer correct to the nearest tenth of a year.

12

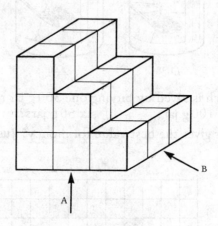

The diagram shows a set of steps which have been made from white plastic cubes of side 30 cm.

(a) Draw what you see when the steps are viewed
    (i) from the direction A,
    (ii) from the direction B.

(b) How many cubes have been used to make this solid? (Assume that the view from A shows the uniform cross-section of the solid.)

(c) Could two solids like this be put together to form a cuboid? If your answer is yes
    (i) how many white plastic cubes have been used,
    (ii) what are the dimensions of the cuboid?

(d) The original solid is painted red and taken apart. How many of the cubes have
    (i) four red faces,
    (ii) three white faces,
    (iii) two red faces?

182

1   (a) Express $\frac{9}{16}$ as (i) a decimal, (ii) a percentage.

    (b) Express as a percentage (i) 3.55 (ii) 0.035

    (c) Write these numbers in order of size, smallest first.

$$0.074 \quad 0.471 \quad 0.47 \quad 0.741$$

2   One whole number is divided by another.

    (a) If the calculator reads `0.6666666`, what could the numbers be?

    (b) If the calculator reads `66.666666`, what could the numbers be?

    (c) If the calculator reads `0.4545454`, what could the numbers be?

    (d) If the calculator reads `45.454545`, what could the numbers be?

3   The sketch shows the net of a cube. The faces of the cube have been marked with spots from one to six.

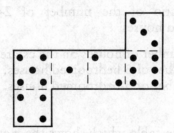

If instead the net had been formed as given below, copy the diagram and mark the spots for the three in their correct position.

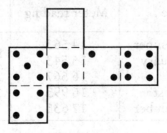

4   Javed walks 1 km along a road that slopes upwards uniformly at 7° to the horizontal. Through what vertical distance, correct to the nearest metre, has he ascended?

5   A wheel is turning at 20 revolutions per minute.

(a) How many revolutions does it make
(i) in 5 minutes,   (ii) in 1 hour?

(b) How many minutes does it take to make
(i) 200 revolutions,   (ii) 5000 revolutions?

6   The pie diagram shows the proportion of a new housing estate alloca-
ted to different sized houses, measured by the number of bedrooms.

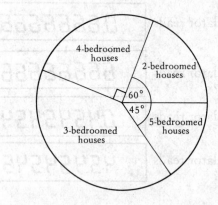

(a) Find the angle of the sector that represents 3-bedroomed houses.

(b) Give the ratio of the number of 2-bedroomed houses to
5–bedroomed houses.

(c) The total number of houses on the estate is 288. Calculate
(i) the number of 5-bedroomed houses,
(ii) the number of 3-bedroomed houses.

7   (a) Complete the table which shows the meter readings in the Smith
household last year.

Date	Meter reading	Number of units used in quarter
6 November	14 563	First
10 February	15 543	Second
4 May	16 567	Third
12 August	16 993	Fourth
8 November	17 635	

(b) If electricity is charged at 8 p per unit in addition to a quarterly
standing charge of £12.25, and if value added tax is added at
8%, find the electricity bill for each quarter.

184

8 The number of goals per match scored by Newtown FC last season are listed below.

$$
\begin{array}{cccccccccc}
1 & 3 & 1 & 0 & 2 & 1 & 3 & 5 & 0 \\
0 & 1 & 0 & 2 & 0 & 1 & 2 & 0 & 1 \\
2 & 1 & 3 & 2 & 4 & 6 & 3 & 5 & 2 \\
4 & 2 & 3 & 3 & 1 & 0 & 1 & 2 & 4 \\
3 & 0 & 4 & 2 & 1 & 1 & 0 & 6 & 5 \\
\end{array}
$$

(a) Copy and complete the following frequency table.

Number of goals scored per match	Tally	Frequency
0		
1		
2		
3		
4		
5		
6		

(b) How many matches did Newtown FC play?

(c) Illustrate this information with a bar chart.

(d) Find the mean, mode and median of this data.

(e) What was the probability that they failed to score in any given match?

9 Draw axes for x and y from 0 to 10 using 1 cm to represent 1 unit. Plot the points A(5, 0), B(1, 2), C(3, 5), D(2, 8) and E(5, 8). Join A to B, B to C, C to D and D to E. Complete the figure so that it is symmetrical about AE. What is the area of the completed figure?

10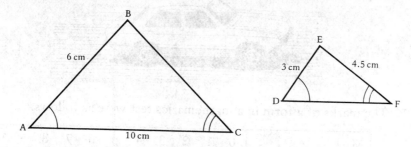

(a) Are triangles ABC and DEF (i) congruent, (ii) similar?

(b) Find (i) the length of BC, (ii) the length of DF.

(c) What is the ratio of the area of $\triangle$ABC to the area of $\triangle$DEF?

Revision Paper

1 I think of a number. I subtract 3 from it. I double the result and my final answer is 22. What number did I think of?

2 Express
   (a) 5240 cm in metres,   (b) 0.493 kg in grams,
   (c) 5000 cm² in square metres,   (d) 1000 mm³ in cubic centimetres.

3 Simplify
   (a) $6 - (-4)$ (b) $(-3) \times (-4)$ (c) $24 \div (-3)$
   (d) $12a + 5a$ (e) $5a \times 3a$ (f) $12a \div 4a$
   (g) $3a^2 \times 4a^3$ (h) $\dfrac{4a^5 \times 2a^2}{8a^8}$ (i) $12a \div (-3a)$.

4 The time in New York is 5 hours behind the time in London. What time is it
   (a) in New York when it is 12 noon in London,
   (b) in London when it is 6 p.m. in New York?

5 Stanley thinks of a number and subtracts three. If he multiplies this result by three the answer is 21. What number did Stanley think of?

6 Peter Snow left home at 8.00 a.m. on a journey of 160 km. He travelled the first 60 km at an average speed of 80 km/hour and the remaining distance at an average speed of 75 km/hour. At what time did he arrive?

7 The marks of a form in a mathematics test were as follows.

Mark	0	1	2	3	4	5	6	7	8	9	10
Number of pupils	0	0	3	1	1	8	8	7	2	2	2

Find
   (a) the mean mark,   (b) the median mark,
   (c) the modal mark,   (d) the range.

8 A soccer team estimates the probability of losing each of five matches. The estimated probabilities are

Match	A	B	C	D	E
Probability of losing	$\frac{99}{100}$	$\frac{3}{4}$	$\frac{3}{5}$	$\frac{1}{2}$	$\frac{1}{50}$

(a) Which of the five matches do the team think
   (i) they are most likely to win,
   (ii) they are most likely to lose?
(b) What is the probability of winning both matches A and B?
(c) What is the probability of losing both matches C and D?

9

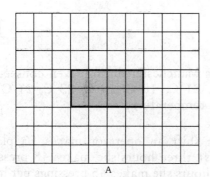

A

B

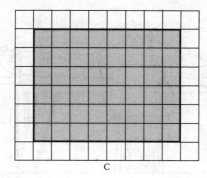

C

A rectangular piece of card measuring 10 cm by 8 cm is to be used to make a small open rectangular box. The diagrams, which are drawn accurately half-size, show three possible ways of doing this. In each case the shaded area becomes the base of the box.

Write down
(a) the dimensions of each box,
(b) the total external surface area of each box,
(c) the volume of each box.

187

10

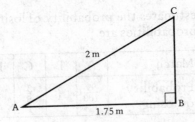

A builder wants to use plastic sheets, 2 m in length, to roof a lean-to shed 1.75 m wide. Find the height of the top end of the sheet C above the level AB.

Revision Paper 13

1 The temperature at midday in Manchester during seven consecutive days was recorded as: 20°C, 21°C, 18°C, 19°C, 23°C, 21°C and 18°C. Find the mean (average) temperature.

2 In the first three hours of a shift an operator makes 53 plastic pressings per hour. In the next three hours she makes 48 pressings per hour and in the final two hours she makes 45 pressings per hour. How many pressings does she make during the eight hour shift?

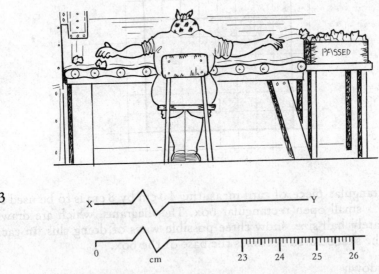

3 The sketch shows a line XY which is measured using a ruler. One end, X, corresponds to 0 on the ruler. The other end, Y, is shown in the sketch. How long is the line XY?

4 Peter Reade wants to put fertiliser on his lawn which is rectangular and measures 18 m by 12 m. The instructions state, 'Use 50 g for each square metre'.

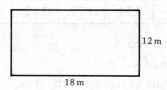

(a) What is the area of the lawn?

(b) How much fertiliser (in kilograms) is required?

(c) How many one kilogram bags of fertiliser must he buy?

5 ABCD is a square, centre O, with E and F points on the side AB, and G and H points on the side BC, such that EF = FG = GH = 3 cm, and OE = OF = OG. M is the midpoint of AB and the figure has rotational symmetry of order 4 about O.

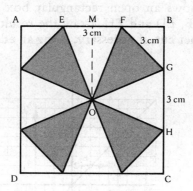

(a) Find
(i) angle BFG, (ii) angle OFG, (iii) angle OFM.

(b) Use Pythagoras' result to find the length of FB, and hence write down the lengths of AB and MB, each correct to 3 s.f.

(c) Write down the length of OM.

(d) Find the area of (i) △OEF (ii) △OFG.

189

6 The age categories of 1000 students in a school are given in the following table.

Age group	11+	12+	13+	14+	15+	16+
Frequency	154	176	182	x	168	132

Use this information to
(a) find the value of x,
(b) draw a bar chart to represent the data,
(c) find the age group in which the median lies,
(d) state the age category with the largest number of students,
(e) state the probability that a pupil chosen at random has had his or her fifteenth birthday.

7

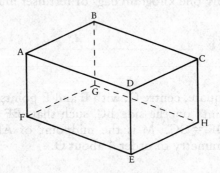

The sketch shows an open rectangular box ABCDEFGH. Cuts are made along EF, ED and EH. Draw the resulting net for this cuboid making a further cut, if necessary, along an edge of the base.

8

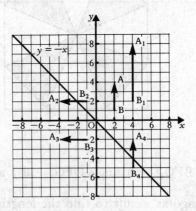

Describe fully the transformation that maps
(a) AB to A_1B_1,
(b) AB to A_2B_2,
(c) AB to A_3B_3,
(d) A_4B_4 to AB,
(e) A_3B_3 to A_2B_2.

9 A multi-storey car park takes $1\frac{1}{2}$ hours to fill at a rate of 6 cars per minute.

   (a) How many cars does it hold?

   (b) How long would it take to fill at a rate of
      (i) 4 cars a minute, (ii) 10 cars a minute?

   (c) From noon, when it is full, until 4 p.m., cars leave at the rate of 8 cars a minute and arrive at the rate of 6 cars a minute. How many cars does the car park hold at 4 p.m.?

10 Given below are the Premier League results and attendances for a Saturday in 1996.

FA Premier	
Coventry (0) . . . . .2 Busst 48, Whelan 84 16,639	**Everton** (0) . . . . .1 Rideout 67
Liverpool (1). . . . . . . .3 Fowler 40, 59, 78 39,806	**Arsenal** (1). . . . . .1 Wright 7 pen.
Man. City (0). 0 28,668	**Chelsea** (0). . . . . .1 Peacock 76
Middlesborough (3) . . .4 Cox 23, Fjortoft 22, Morris 29, Hendrie 85	**West Ham** (0) . . . . .2 Cottee 81, Dicks 89 28,640
Newcastle (2). . . . . . . .3 Ginola 26, Lee 11, 47 36,531	**Nottm Forest** (1) . . . . . .1 Woan 14
QPR (0). . . . . .1 Gallen 54	**Aston Villa** (0) 0 14,778
Sheff. Wed. (1). . . . . . .2 Hirst 14 pen., 50 pen. 25,115	**Southampton** (1). . . . . .2 Heaney 7, Magilton 80 pen.
Tottenham (0). . . . . . . .2 Armstrong 71, Sheringham 54	**Bolton** (0). . . . . .2 Bergsson 79, Green 76 30,702
Wimbledon (0) . . . . . . .1 Earle 83 7,105	**Blackburn** (1). . . . . . . .1 Kimble 27 o.g.
Leeds (2) . . . . .3 Dean 73, McAllister 6 pen., Yeboah 36	**Man. Utd** (1). . . . . .1 Cole 39,801

   (a) How many spectators watched Premier League football that Saturday?

   (b) How many spectators watched the home side win that Saturday?

   (c) What was the average gate?

   (d) Make a frequency table to show the number of teams scoring 0 goals, 1 goal, 2 goals, etc.

   (e) Find the mean, mode and median number of goals scored per team.

Revision Paper 14

1 The attendance at an international match was 54 494. What was the attendance correct to
   (a) the nearest thousand,   (b) the nearest hundred,
   (c) three significant figures,   (d) the nearest ten thousand?

2 The dimensions of a rectangular table top are given as 120 cm by 82 cm, each dimension being correct to the nearest centimetre.
   (a) What is the longest possible length of the table?
   (b) What is the shortest possible width of the table?
   (c) What is the largest possible area of the tabletop?
   (d) What is the smallest possible area of the tabletop?

3 The diagram shows the reading on a bathroom scale when John stood on it one morning. How heavy is he?

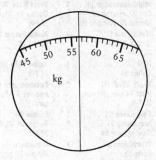

4 John's calculator has a fault. The + button is marked X and the X button is marked + . He wants to find the value of (15 + 2) X (8 − 3).
   (a) What answer does John get using his calculator?
   (b) What is the correct answer?

5 The time in Moscow is 3 hours ahead of London time, while the time in Toronto is 5 hours behind London time. What time is it
   (a) in Moscow when it is 10 a.m. in Toronto,
   (b) in Toronto when it is midnight in Moscow?

6 A motorcycle is offered for sale at £2240. If bought on credit terms, a deposit of $\frac{1}{4}$ is required together with 24 monthly payments of £85.96. Find

(a) the credit sale price,

(b) the difference between the cash price and the credit sale price.

7

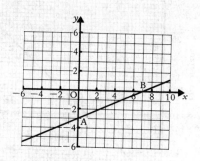

The equation of the straight line AB is $3x - 7y + 21 = 0$.

(a) What is the gradient of AB?

(b) Copy the diagram and sketch the region defined by the two inequalities $7y - 3x \geqslant 21$ and $x \geqslant 0$.

8 Laura wishes to find, correct to one decimal place, a solution of the equation $3x^2 = 8$.

When $x = 1.8$, she works out the value of $3x^2$ as $3 \times (1.8)^2 = 9.72$.

When $x = 1.5$, she works out the value of $3x^2$ as $3 \times (1.5)^2 = 6.75$.

Find the value of $3x^2$ when (a) $x = 1.7$, (b) $x = 1.6$. What do you think was Laura's solution to the equation?

9 The perimeter of a door ABCD is 5.4 m.

(a) Write down, in terms of x, an expression for the area of one side of the door.

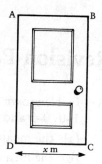

(b) If the area of one side of the door is 1.6 m² show that $x^2 - 2.7x + 1.6 = 0$.

(c) Complete the table of values for $y = x^2 - 2.7x + 1.6$.

x	0	0.25	0.5	0.75	1	1.25
y		0.99	0.5	0.14		-0.21

Draw the graph of $y = x^2 - 2.7x + 1.6$ for values of x from 0 to 1.25, taking 8 cm as 1 unit on the x-axis and 10 cm as 1 unit on the y-axis.

(d) Read off from your graph an approximate value for the width of the door.

193

10 The conversion graph shows the rate of exchange from United Kingdom pounds to French francs.

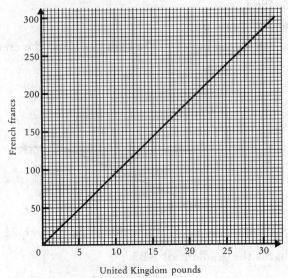

(a) Use the graph to find
  (i) the value of £20 in French francs,
  (ii) the value of 175 French francs in pounds sterling,
  (iii) the value of £1 in French francs.

(b) One year later the exchange rate has changed so that £1 is equivalent to 8 French francs. Draw a line to represent this on the graph.

(c) Does the change in the exchange rate favour the French tourist in Britain or the British tourist in France?

Revision Paper   15

1 In Newtown Utd's last five home games the scores were 3-0, 2-3, 1-0, 0-3 and 4-2. Find
  (a) the mean number of goals for,
  (b) the mean number of goals against.

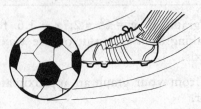

2   Jenny spent $\frac{1}{4}$ of her pocket money on a lipstick, $\frac{1}{3}$ of the *remainder* on sweets, and £1.10 on a magazine. If she still had £2.50 left find
    (a) the amount of pocket money she received,
    (b) the amount she spent on the lipstick,
    (c) the amount she spent on sweets.

3   (a) Mr and Mrs Green borrow £54 000 from a building society when they move to a larger house. The repayments are £11.37 per calendar month per £1000 borrowed. Calculate their monthly repayments.
    (b) Janet Burris buys a bottle of perfume in the duty-free shop at Rome airport for 27 600 lire. If £1 ≡ 2300 L, how much does she save if a similar bottle is selling for £14.80 in London?

4   (a) Write these numbers in order of size, largest first.
                0.23   0.32   0.032   0.321
    (b) In each case, give the range within which each measurement lies.
        (i)   Ted's age, rounded down to the nearest year, is 16.
        (ii) The length of a rope, rounded to the nearest metre, is 30 m.
        (iii) The weight of a dog, correct to the nearest kilogram, is 20 kg.

5   A rectangular piece of wood measuring 25 cm by x cm is to be sawn into eighteen identical squares. Each saw cut is 2 mm wide.

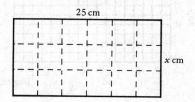

25 cm

x cm

    (a) Find the length of the side of one of the square pieces.
    (b) Find x.

6

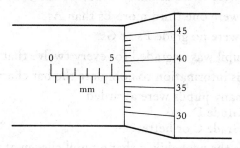

    This micrometer can be used to obtain readings correct to the nearest hundredth of a millimetre. What reading does it show in the sketch?

7 The cooking instructions for cooking pork using Gas Mark 3 are 50 minutes per pound plus 50 minutes over.

(a) How long will it take to cook a joint of pork weighing
    (i) 3 lb,   (ii) 7 lb?

(b) Find a formula to give the time, M minutes, to cook a joint weighing W lb.

(c) Give your answer to part (b) in hours.

8 In a sale Gamleys Department Store offer 15p in the £ off all marked prices.

(a) How much must Judith pay for a dress marked £80?

(b) Peter paid £127.50 for a compact disc player. What was the marked price?

9 The bar chart shows the number of pupils from Pontford Comprehensive School who obtained Grades A, B or C in mathematics last summer.

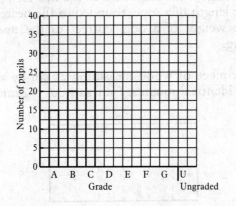

The remaining pupils were awarded grades as follows

   there were twice as many Grade Ds as Grade Bs,

   there were one third more Es than As,

   there were no grade Fs or Gs,

   one pupil was ungraded for every twelve that were graded.

(a) Use this information to complete the bar chart.

(b) How many pupils were awarded
    (i) a Grade D,
    (ii) a Grade C or better?

(c) What is the probability that a pupil chosen at random from these pupils
    (i) was awarded a Grade D,
    (ii) was awarded a Grade B or better?

196

10 The sketch shows a rectangular white flag with a red band across it.

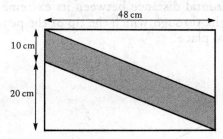

    48 cm

10 cm

20 cm

(a) What shape is the red band?

(b) Find the area of
    (i) the band,
    (ii) the flag,
    (iii) one of the triangular sections.

(c) Express the area of the band as a fraction of the area of the whole flag.

Revision Paper

16

1 (a) How many sides are there in
    (i) a pentagon, (ii) an octagon, (iii) a trapezium?

  (b) How many interior angles are there in
    (i) a rhombus, (ii) a hexagon?

  (c) Find the size of
    (i) an exterior angle,
    (ii) an interior angle, in a regular polygon with 12 sides.

  (d) The exterior angle of a regular polygon is 15°. How many sides does it have?

2 The area of a trapezium is given by the formula $A = \left(\dfrac{a+b}{2}\right)h$.

  (a) Find A when $a = 8$ cm, $b = 11$ cm and $h = 4$ cm.

  (b) Find h in terms of A, a and b.

  (c) Find a in terms of A, b and h.

3 Remove the brackets and simplify

  (a) $3(5x - 2) + 2(2x + 7)$ (b) $(5x - 2)(2x + 7)$

  (c) $(5x - 2)^2$,   (d) $(3x - 4)(4x - 3)$.

4 Solve the equations

  (a) $5x + 7 = 17$ (b) $8x - 5 = 5x + 4$

  (c) $3(x - 2) + 2(x + 1) = 16$ (d) $\dfrac{x}{5} + 7 = 10$.

5   The pendulum of a clock is 100 cm long and swings to and fro so that the horizontal distance between its extreme positions is 12 cm. Find the height through which the tip of the pendulum rises, correct to one decimal place.

6

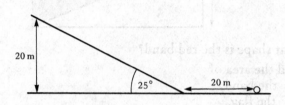

Phillip's football rolls over the edge of a bank that is 20 m high and rolls uniformly at an angle of 25° with the horizontal. It comes to rest 20 m further on than the base of the bank. How far does he have to walk to retrieve it?

7

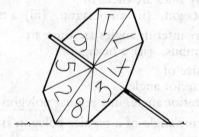

The spinning disc shown in the diagram is made from a regular octagon and is numbered 1 to 8 as shown. It comes to rest after being spun with one of the eight edges resting on the table. The number on the triangle with this edge is the score.

(a) What is the sum of opposite numbers?

(b) Find the probability that a single score is
       (i) an even number,   (ii) a prime number,
       (iii) a triangular number,   (iv) a perfect square.

(c) What is the probability that the sum of the scores for two consecutive spins is
       (i) 16,   (ii) more than 14,   (iii) 20?

198

8

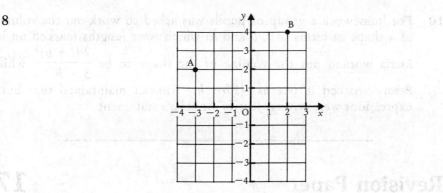

(a) Write down the coordinates of A and B.

(b) C is the point $(2, -4)$. Copy the diagram and mark point C.

(c) The quadrilateral ABCD is symmetrical about the x-axis. What are the coordinates of D? Draw ABCD on your diagram.

(d) E is the point on BC such that AE is perpendicular to BC. What are the coordinates of E?

(e) AEFD is a rectangle. Write down the coordinates of F.

(f) Find the area of
(i) $\triangle$ABE,   (ii) rectangle AEFD,   (iii) $\triangle$DFC
(iv) quadrilateral ABCD.

9

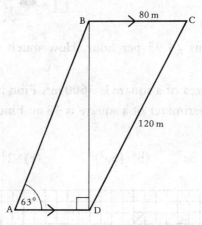

ABCD represents a field in the shape of a trapezium with AD parallel to BC. BC = 80 m, DC = 120 m, $A\hat{D}B = 90°$ and $B\hat{A}D = 63°$.
Find

(a) the size of angle BCD,

(b) the length of BD,

(c) the length of AD,

(d) the area of ABCD
(i) in m^2 (ii) in hectares (1 hectare = 10 000 m^2).

199

10 For homework a group of pupils was asked to work out the volume of a shape in terms of l, b and h, which were lengths marked on it. Maria worked out the volume of the shape to be $\dfrac{2}{3}\dfrac{(l+b)^2}{h}$ while Penny worked it out as $\frac{2}{3}l^2b + h$. Anneka maintained that both expressions were wrong. Justify Anneka's statement.

Revision Paper   17

1 (a) Write these numbers in order of size, smallest first.

    0.315   0.33   0.066   0.373

   (b) Express
        (i) 0.22 cm in mm, (ii) 5400cm^2 in m^2, (iii) 0.0003 m^3 in cm^3.

2 Mrs Walker insures her house for £90 000. The premium is £1.25 per £1000 of cover. What is her total premium?

3 Steve earns £4.95 per hour. How much will he earn for 40 hours work?

4 (a) The area of a square is 3600 m^2. Find its perimeter.
   (b) The perimeter of a square is 48 m. Find its area.

5 Simplify
   (a) $5a^2 \times 3a^3$ (b) $(3a^2)^3$ (c) 2^3 (d) $\sqrt{\dfrac{25}{36}}$

6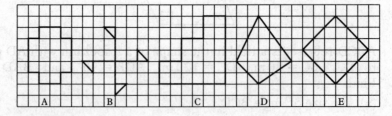

   Which of these shapes have
   (a) line symmetry,
   (b) rotational symmetry,
   (c) neither line nor rotational symmetry?

7 If $y = \dfrac{3(x-5)}{7}$ find

(a) y when $x = 54$ (b) x when $y = 27$.

8

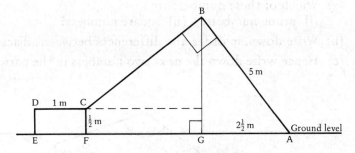

The diagram represents a playground slide. Use the information on the diagram to find

(a) the height of B, the top of the slide, above the ground,

(b) the size of angle ABG,

(c) the angle between BC and the horizontal,

(d) the length, BC, of the sloping part of the slide,

(e) the total distance from A to E.

9 Four boys, Arthur, Bernard, Clive and Don, are to compete in the final of the school's 100 m and 200 m. The probabilities that each will win are given in the following table.

	A	B	C	D
100 m	$\dfrac{1}{12}$	$\dfrac{1}{6}$	$\dfrac{1}{4}$	$\dfrac{1}{2}$
200 m	$\dfrac{1}{8}$	$\dfrac{1}{8}$	$\dfrac{3}{8}$	$\dfrac{3}{8}$

(a) Which boy is considered the best overall sprinter?

(b) What is the probability that Arthur will win both races?

(c) What is the probability that Don will not win the 200 m?

10 The school grounds are in the shape of a quadrilateral ABCD with AB = 300 m, BC = 200 m, CD = 350 m, $A\widehat{B}C = 120°$ and $B\widehat{C}D = 90°$. Using a scale of 1 cm to 25 m make an accurate scale drawing of the grounds.

Use your drawing to find the length of the fourth side of the quadrilateral.

Revision Paper

18

1 The first six numbers in a pattern are 3, 8, 16, 27, 41, 58.
   (a) Which of these numbers are
       (i) prime numbers,   (ii) square numbers?
   (b) Write down, in order, the differences between adjacent numbers.
   (c) Hence write down the next two numbers in the pattern.

2

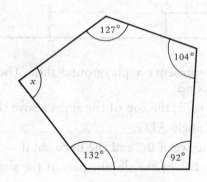

   Find the unknown angle in the given pentagon.

3 (a) If x is an even number, what is the sum of the next two odd
       numbers?
   (b) Simplify
       (i) $2a^3 \times 6a^2$ (ii) $12a^9 \div 4a^6$ (iii) $(2a^2b)^2 \times 3ab^4$.

4 A department store advertises a suite at £2100. Three different
   arrangements are offered if it is bought on credit.

       1. a deposit of $\frac{1}{3}$ plus 12 monthly payments of £127.75,
       2. a deposit of $\frac{1}{4}$ plus 12 monthly payments of £144.12,
       3. a deposit of $\frac{1}{5}$ plus 12 monthly payments of £151.73.

   Which is
   (a) the cheapest,   (b) the dearest,   of these arrangements?

5 A table tennis ball is dropped from a height of 810 cm. On the first
   bounce it rises to a height of 270 cm, and on the second bounce it
   rises to a height of 90 cm. To what height would you expect it to
   rise
   (a) on the third bounce,   (b) on the fourth bounce?

6 If I plant a certain flower seed, the probability that it will grow is $\frac{9}{10}$. The probability that one which has grown will bear flowers is $\frac{11}{12}$.

(a) What is the probability that a seed planted will not grow?

(b) What is the probability that a plant that has grown will not bear flowers?

(c) What is the probability that a seed will grow and bear flowers?

(d) If I plant 280 seeds, how many flower-bearing plants should I expect?

7

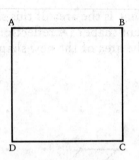 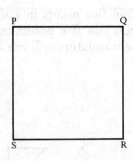

What is the image of A in the square PQRS, when the square ABCD is transformed into PQRS by

(a) a reflection in XY,   (b) a translation?

8

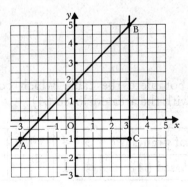

Write down

(a) the coordinates of the three points A, B and C,

(b) the equation of (i) AC (ii) BC,

(c) the gradient of AB,

(d) the equation of the straight line that passes through the origin and is parallel to AB.

9   The smallest number of straight lines that will enclose a space is three. Three straight lines give a triangle. In what follows *no dot may appear within a shape.*

On dotted paper join three points to make a triangle. The area of this triangle is $\frac{1}{2}$ a square unit.

If four points are joined the figure may be a square or a parallelogram, both of which are shown in the diagram. The area of each shape is 1 square unit.

Join five points in a similar way. What is the area of this shape? Can you join five points to give a different shape? (A reflection, rotation or translation will not do.) What is the area of the new shape?

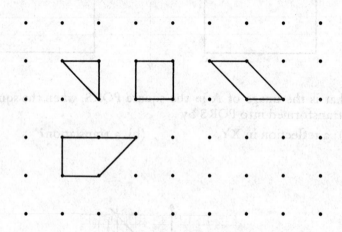

(a) Copy and complete the table which connects the number of points (*P*) with the area enclosed (*A*).

Number of points (P)	3	4	5	6	7	8	9	10	11	12
Area enclosed (A)	$\frac{1}{2}$	1								

(b) Write down a formula connecting *A* and *P*. Use this formula to find
    (i) the area enclosed if 20 points are joined,
    (ii) the number of points joined when the area is 12 square units.

(c) Write down a formula connecting *A* and *P* with *P* as the subject.

204

10 (a) Copy and complete the following table which gives the values of $4x^2$ for values of x in the range -3 to 3.

x	-3	-2.5	-2	-1.5	-1	-0.5	0	0.5	1	1.5	2	2.5	3
$4x^2$	36	25				1	0	1		9		25	

Using 4 cm as 1 unit on the x-axis and 4 cm as 10 units on the y-axis, draw the graph of $y = 4x^2$.

(b) Use your graph to find the values of x when $y = 20$.

(c) On the same axes draw the graph of $y = 5x + 10$. Write down the values of x at the points of intersection of the two graphs.

Revision Paper 19

1 (a) If $a = 2.4 \times 10^5$ and $b = 6 \times 10^3$ write down the value of each letter as an ordinary number.

(b) Hence find (i) $a + b$ (ii) $a - b$.

(c) Express your answers to part (b) in standard form.

2 In eight consecutive completed innings a batsman's scores were 42, 18, 64, 137, 8, 54, 95 and 38. Find his average score. In his next innings he scores 88 not out. What is his new average?

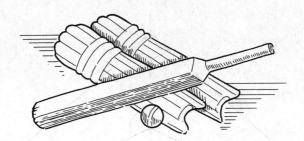

3 (a) (b) 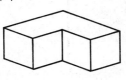 (c)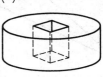

How many planes of symmetry does each solid have?

4   (a) Find (i) 70% of £8.40 (ii) 3.5% of 550 g.

　　(b) How many times does $\frac{3}{8}$ go into 9?

　　(c) Express $\dfrac{2^4 \times 2^2}{2^8}$ as a single power of 2.

5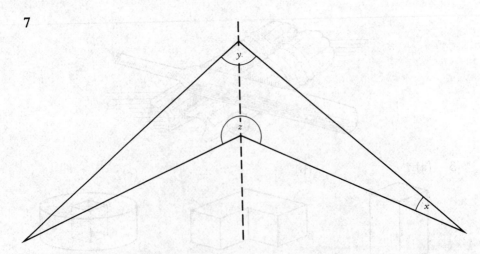

ABC and DEF are triangles with equal angles marked. AB = 6 cm, AC = 12 cm, BC = 9 cm and EF = 6 cm. Find

　　(a) DE and DF

　　(b) the ratio $\dfrac{\triangle ABC}{\triangle DEF}$.

6   If a letter is taken at random from the word SCIENTIST, what is the probability that it is

　　(a) a vowel,　　　(b) a consonant,　　　(c) the letter T?

7

The diagram shows a chevron, from a road sign, that has one axis of symmetry. Use your protractor to find the sizes of the angles marked with letters. What is the sum of the four angles within the chevron?

206

8 The temperatures taken at two-hourly intervals on a certain day are given in the following table.

Time	Mid-night	2 a.m.	4 a.m.	6 a.m.	8 a.m.	10 a.m.	Noon
Temperature (°C)	2.4	1.7	1.2	2.4	7.4	12.2	15.8

Time	2 p.m.	4 p.m.	6 p.m.	8 p.m.	10 p.m.	Mid-night
Temperature (°C)	17.2	16.8	15	10.6	6	3

Draw a graph to show this data taking $2 \text{ cm} \equiv 2$ hours and $2 \text{ cm} \equiv 2°C$. From your graph determine

(a) the temperature at 9 a.m.,

(b) the times at which the temperature was $9°C$.

9 (a) The equation of a curve is $y = 3x^2 + 2$. Which of these sketches best shows the curve?

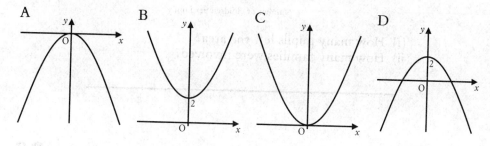

(b) Sketch, on the same axes, the graphs of
   (i) $y = 2x^2$
   (ii) $y = -2x^2$
   (iii) $y = 2x^2 - 3$
   (iv) $y = 3 - 2x^2$
   clearly distinguishing between them.

(c) Describe the transformation that
   (i) maps the first curve in part (b) into the second curve,
   (ii) maps the third curve into the first.

10   A class of 30 pupils was asked, 'How many children are there in your family?'. An incomplete table listing the results is given below.

Number of children in family	1	2	3	4	5
Number of pupils		12	6	2	1

(a)   (i) How many of the pupils in the class are only children?
      (ii) What percentage of the class belong to a family with two children?

(b) The bar chart shows the number of children per family after some of the pupils had left the area to move to another part of the country.

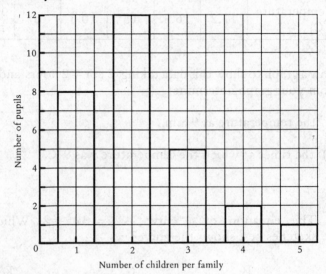

Number of children per family

(i) How many pupils left the area?
(ii) How many families were involved?

Revision Paper   20

1   Complete the following table.

Fraction	Decimal	Percentage
$\frac{1}{2}$	0.5	50%
$\frac{1}{4}$		
	0.8	
		75%

2   (a) Solve the equations
        (i) $(x - 7)(x + 4) = 0$ (ii) $x^2 - 7x + 12 = 0$.
    (b) Express 37.537 correct to
        (i) three significant figures,
        (ii) two decimal places,
        (iii) the nearest whole number.

3   Insert one of the symbols $>$, $=$ or $<$ correctly in
    (a) $\frac{3}{4} + \frac{1}{3}$ $\frac{4}{7}$ (b) $5^2 - 4^2$ 3^2
    (c) $5^2 \times 4^2$ 20^2 (d) $6^2 \div 3^2$ 3^2

4

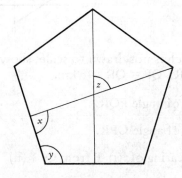

The figure shows a regular pentagon with two of its axes of symmetry.
(a) What is the size of an exterior angle of this pentagon?
(b) Find the sizes of the angles marked x, y and z.

5

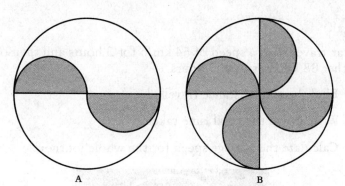

A   B

The diagrams show two possible designs for planting bulbs to give red
tulips (shaded) and bulbs to give yellow tulips (unshaded) in a circular
bed of diameter 5 m. If design A is chosen 1500 red tulip bulbs are
needed.

Assuming that bulbs for red and yellow tulips each require equal
ground area for planting find the number of yellow tulip bulbs
required
(a) for design A,   (b) for design B.

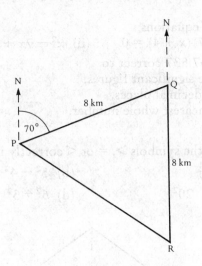

The diagram, which is not drawn to scale, shows the position of three villages P, Q and R. QP = QR = 8 km.

(a) Find the size of angle PQR.

(b) Find the size of angle QPR.

(c) What is the bearing of (i) P from Q,   (ii) P from R?

(d) Draw a scale drawing to show the positions of P, Q and R using 1 cm to represent 1 km.

(e) Use your diagram to find the shortest distance from P to the straight road that joins Q to R.

7   A car travelled at a speed of 54 km/h for 3 hours and then travelled a further 88 kilometres in 2 hours.

(a) Find the total distance travelled.

(b) Write down the total time taken.

(c) Calculate the average speed for the whole journey.

8 (a) State whether each of the following quantities should be measured in length, area or volume units.
    (i) the surface of a cube,
    (ii) the space inside a rectangular box,
    (iii) the distance round the edge of a table.

  (b) The letters b, l, w and h each represent a number of centimetres. Write down a suitable unit (e.g. cm^3) for the subject of each of the following formulas.
    (i) $P = 3lb + 2bh$
    (ii) $Q = 2l + 2w$
    (iii) $R = 2lbh$
    (iv) $S = 4\pi l^2$

  (c) In the formulas that follow, P represents a number of units of length, A a number of units of area and V a number of units of volume. Each of the other letters represents a number of units of length. State which formulas must be incorrect.
    (i) $A = p^2 + q^2$
    (ii) $V = P + A$
    (iii) $V = a^2 b + 2b^3$
    (iv) $P = 2pq$
    (v) $P = a + 3b - 2c^2$
    (vi) $A = p^2 + 3qr$

9 (a) Mary's birthday is in June. What is the probability that
    (i) the date will divide exactly by 5,
    (ii) it is an even date,
    (iii) the date is not divisible by 3?

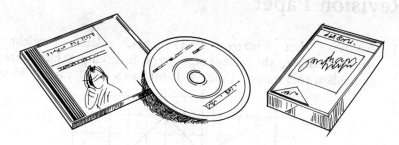

  (b) One box contains two cassettes and three CDs. Another box contains three cassettes and one CD. Draw a possibility space showing the various ways in which two items can be chosen, one from each box. Use your possibility space to find the probability that
    (i) both items are cassettes,
    (ii) both are CDs.

10 The table below shows the cost (in £) of a 7-night and 14-night holiday for one person self-catering in Tenerife, Rhodes and Crete.

	Tenerife		Rhodes		Crete	
Number of days	7	14	7	14	7	14
May	304	369	308	420	333	496
June	324	394	355	471	385	554
July	373	451	390	511	444	624
August	398	463	381	501	456	635
September	363	442	355	475	421	605

(a) Write down the cost of a 14-night holiday in Rhodes during June.

(b) Find the difference between the cost in August and the cost in September of a 14-night holiday for one person in Crete.

(c) Find the total cost of a 7-night holiday for a family of four adults during August in Tenerife.

The reduction for children under 12 years of age is 40% in June and September, and 20% during the other months.

(d) What is the cost of a 14-night holiday in Crete for a family of two adults and a 10-year-old child in August?

(e) How much cheaper is it for an eight-year-old child to be taken to Crete for a 14-night holiday in September rather than in August?

(f) A family consists of father, mother and three children aged 10, 12 and 14. How much will a 14-night holiday in Rhodes cost them in July?

Revision Paper   21

1 Assuming that 1 metre = 39.37 inches, calculate, to the nearest whole number, the percentage error in taking 8 kilometres to be equivalent to 5 miles. (1 mile = 1760 yards and 1 yard = 36 inches.)

2

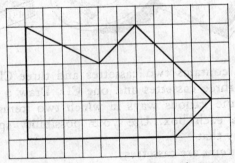

Copy the figure given above on to squared paper.

(a) Using the grid as a guide, draw this figure
  (i) half-size,
  (ii) when it is enlarged by a factor of 2.

(b) In part (a), by what factor has the area changed in each one?

3 A shopkeeper sells goods so as to make a profit of 40% on the cost price. Use this information to complete the following table.

Cost price	Profit	Selling price
£50		
	£24	
		£105

4 The diagram represents a triangular field. AB = 4 cm and the length of the dotted line is also 4 cm.

(a) If the scale of the map is 1 : 50 000, find the area of the field in
  (i) m²
  (ii) hectares (1 hectare = 10 000 m²).

(b) If the area of the field is 5000 m², what is the scale of the map?

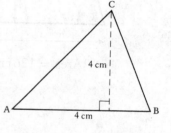

5

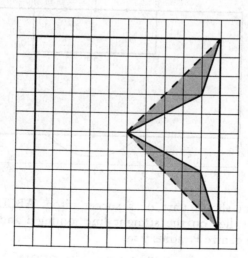

The diagram shows one quarter of a pattern that has four axes of symmetry.

(a) Complete the diagram and mark, with dotted lines, the axes of symmetry.

(b) What fraction of the completed diagram is shaded?

6 For each of these shapes the area, together with one dimension, is given. Find each dimension marked with a letter.

(a)

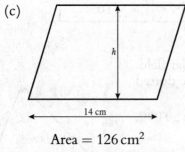

Area = 192 mm²

(b)

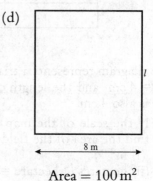

12 cm

b

Area = 108 cm²

(c)

h

14 cm

Area = 126 cm²

(d)

l

8 m

Area = 100 m²

7

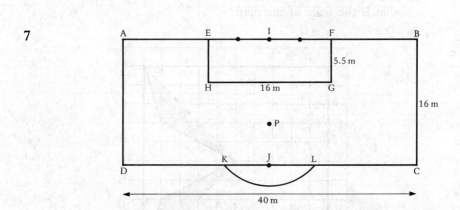

The diagram shows part of a soccer pitch. ABCD and EFGH are rectangles; P lies on the straight line joining I and J, and KL is an arc of circle centre P radius 9 m.

(a) Calculate the area of (i) ABCD (ii) EFGH.

(b) If the penalty spot, P, is 5.5 m from HG how far is it from DC?

(c) Find (i) the length of JL, (ii) the size of angle JPL.

(d) Find the distance of P from (i) B (ii) C (iii) F.

214

8 The positive number n satisfies the equation $n^2 + 2n = 75$.

(a) Write down two consecutive positive whole numbers between which n must lie.

(b) Use your calculator to find the value of n correct to three significant figures.

9 Given below is part of an Inter City 125 timetable.

Mondays to Saturdays

	125	B125	D125	125	125	B125	D125	125	125	D
London Paddington	0655	0800	0800	0900	0930	0950	1000	1100	1200	1210
Slough (depart)	0709	——	——	——	0855	1004	——	——	1125	——
Reading (depart)	0723	0824	0824	0924	0954	1018	——	1124	1224	1241
Swindon	0755	——	0852	——	——	1050	——	1152	1252	——
Bristol Parkway	0819	0911	0916	1010	——	1114	1106	1216	1316	——
Newport	0842	0935	0939	1033	1059	1137	1129	1239	1339	1402
Cardiff Central	0858	0952	0955	1049	1115	1153	1145	1255	1355	1419
Bridgend	0920	1014	1016	1110	——	1214	1206	1316	1416	——
Port Talbot Parkway	0934	1028	1030	1124	——	1228	1220	1330	1430	——
Neath	0941	1035	1037	1131	——	1235	1227	1337	1437	——
Swansea	0956	1050	1052	1146	——	1250	1242	1352	1452	——

Mondays to Saturdays

	125	125	125	125	125	B125	B125	D125	125	C
London Paddington	1300	1400	1500	1535	1600	1640	1720	1720	1800	1809
Slough (depart)	——	——	1425	1549	——	1638	——	1700	1726	——
Reading (depart)	1324	1424	1524	1603	——	1702	——	1744	1823	1841
Swindon	1352	1452	1552p	1635	——	1732	——	1812	——	——
Bristol Parkway	1416	1516	1616	1659	1706	1756	1826	1836	1911	1943
Newport	1439	1539	1639	——	1729	1819	1849	1859	1935	2008
Cardiff Central	1455	1555	1655	——	1745	1835	1905	1915	1952	2025
Bridgend	1516	1616	1716	——	1806	1856	1926	1936	2014	2049
Port Talbot Parkway	1530	1630	1730	——	1820	1910	1940	1950	2028	2105
Neath	1537	1637	1737	——	1827	1917	1947	1957	2035	2113
Swansea	1552	1652	1752	——	1842	1933	2002	2012	2050	2133

Use this timetable to answer the following questions.

(a) How long does the 0900 train from Paddington take to reach Cardiff?

(b) How long does the 0950 from Paddington take to travel from Reading to Newport?

(c) Sally wishes to get to Swindon by 1730. What is the latest she can leave Paddington? How long will the train journey take?

(d) How many trains leaving Reading between 0800 and 1200 inclusive stop at Swindon?

(e) Which train gives the fastest journey from Paddington to Bristol Parkway — the 0900, the 1000 or the 1300?

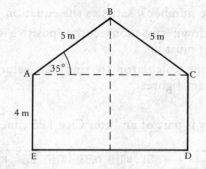

The diagram shows the cross-section through a shed. $AB = BC = 5$ metres, $AE = CD = 4$ metres and $\angle BAC = 35°$. Calculate

(a) AC,

(b) the height of the ridge B above the ground.

Revision Paper 22

1 If $s = (u + v)t$ find
   (a) the value of s when $u = 4$, $v = 12$ and $t = 3$,
   (b) the value of t when $s = 60$, $u = 5$ and $v = 7$,
   (c) the value of u when $s = 32$, $v = 5$ and $t = 4$.

2 (a) Express 1296 as the product of its prime factors.
   (b) Hence find the square root of 1296.

3 Add 5.46 cm^2 to 768 mm^2 and give the answer in cm^2.

4 Factorise
   (a) $3x^2 + 9$ (b) $3x^2 + 9x$
   (c) $x^2 + 2x - 24$ (d) $x^2 - 9$.

5 The table shows how a married man spends his weekly wage.

Food	Clothes	Mortgage	Car	Services	Leisure	Savings
£80	£16	£100	£50	£20	£50	£44

   (a) Find his weekly wage.
   (b) Draw and label a pie diagram to represent this information. Use a circle of radius 5 cm.

6 A couple buy a car by borrowing £5000 from a credit company. They agree to repay £150 each month after interest of 2% per month has been added to their debt. How much do they owe after

(a) 2 payments, (b) 6 payments?

7 The marked price of a three-piece suite is £2580. A 5% discount is offered for a cash sale, but if bought on credit, the deposit is $\frac{1}{3}$, followed by 18 monthly payments of £114.66. Find the difference in cost between the two ways of paying for the suite, and express this difference as a percentage of the *cash* price, giving your answer correct to three significant figures.

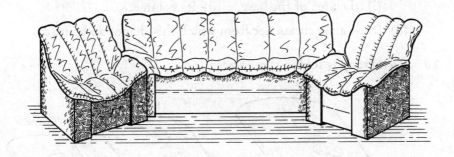

8

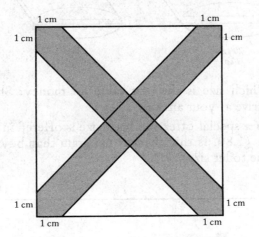

The diagram shows a square white flag of side 6 cm with two diagonal bands as shown in the diagram. Find

(a) the area of one of the diagonal bands,

(b) the width of each band, correct to 3 s.f.,

(c) the shaded area,

(d) the unshaded area.

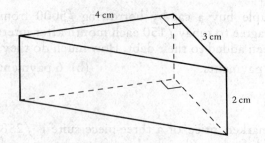

9

(a) What name do we give to this three dimensional shape which has a uniform cross-section?

(b) How many (i) faces, (ii) edges, (iii) vertices, does it have?

(c) Use the measurements given on the sketch to find
(i) the area of the base, (ii) its volume.

(d) Draw an accurate net from which this shape can be made.

10 Royal soap is sold in three sizes.

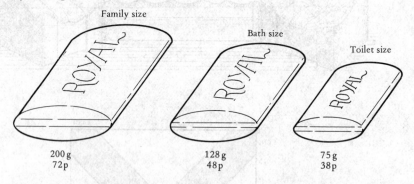

(a) Which size is the best value for money? Show clearly how you arrive at your answer.

(b) In a special offer the bath size is offered in packs of four tablets at £1.80. Is this cheaper per gram than buying the family size or the toilet size?

Revision Paper 23

1 (a) Find the simple interest on £540 when it is invested for 5 years at 12%.

(b) Find the compound interest earned if £700 is invested for 2 years at 8% per annum.

2 (a) Use your calculator to evaluate
(i) 600×1.14 (ii) $600 \times 1.14 \times 1.14$.

(b) The temperature of the water in a jug is 19 °C correct to the nearest degree. If the temperature of this water had been given in degrees Fahrenheit, correct to the nearest degree, what values might have been given for the temperature?

3　(a)　If $(2x + 1)(x - 4) = ax^2 + bx + c$ find the values of a, b and c.
　(b)　If $x^2 - 2x - 15 = (x + a)(x + b)$ find the values of a and b.

4　For each pair of variables named below, state whether they are positively correlated, negatively correlated or uncorrelated.
　(a)　The waist measurements and weights of adult males of similar height.
　(b)　The mileometer (odometer) reading of a car and its age.
　(c)　The daily sale of deck chair tickets at a holiday resort and the daily rainfall at that resort.
　(d)　The weights and maths marks of a group of 16-year-old schoolboys.

5　(a)　Express 55 g as a percentage of 2 kg.
　(b)　Increase £4.20 by 30%.

6　Construct a triangle ABC in which AB = 13.6 cm, BC = 8.5 cm and $\widehat{ABC} = 60°$. Measure and write down the length of AC.

7　A newly-married couple bought a house for £54 000. It increased in value by 3% each year. How much was it worth
　(a)　2 years later,　　　　　　　(b)　5 years later?

8　The diagram shows a tessellation of a rhombus.

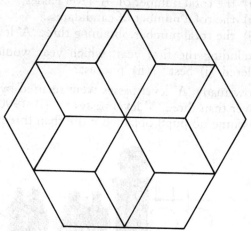

　(a)　Copy this tessellation and extend it on the right-hand side by adding at least six more rhombuses.
　(b)　Find the sizes of the four angles in one of these rhombuses.

9   The graph shows the 'A' level results for Seagrave School since 1988.

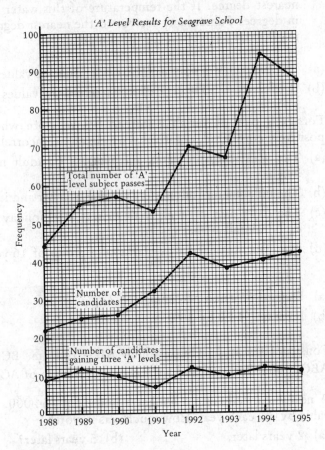

'A' Level Results for Seagrave School

(a) What is the general trend in
   (i) the total number of 'A' level passes,
   (ii) the total number of candidates,
   (iii) the total number obtaining three 'A' level passes?

(b) Excluding the first year, which year would the results be considered (i) best, (ii) poorest?

(c) How many 'A' level passes were secured by candidates who had fewer than three 'A' level passes in (i) 1990, (ii) 1994?
   (Assume no pupil obtained more than three 'A' level passes.)

10

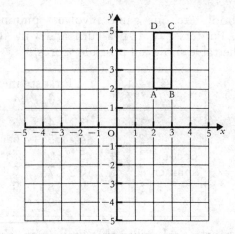

The rectangle ABCD is reflected in the y-axis to give the rectangle $A_1B_1C_1D_1$, in the x-axis to give the rectangle $A_2B_2C_2D_2$, and rotated about the origin through $180°$ to give the rectangle $A_3B_3C_3D_3$. Show, in the same diagram, the three new positions of the rectangle.

Revision Paper

24

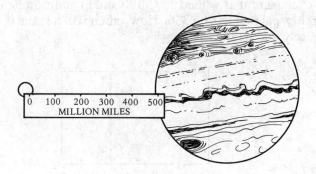

1 (a) The mean distance of the planet Jupiter from the Earth is 483 million miles. Express this distance in standard form.

   (b) The diameter of a particle is 0.000 005 2 cm. Express this in standard form (i) in cm   (ii) in m.

2   Solve the equations

   (a) $\dfrac{3x}{4} - 1 = 5$ (b) $\dfrac{3x - 1}{4} = 5$ (c) $\dfrac{3(x - 1)}{4} = 5$

3   At a school fête one game involves spinning a pair of hexagonal spinners. Punters pay 10p a turn and win 40p if they score 10 or more. The table shows all possible scores.

		First spinner					
		1	2	3	4	5	6
	1	2	3	4	5	6	7
	2	3	4	5	6	7	8
Second	3	4	5	6	7	8	9
spinner	4	5	6	7	8	9	10
	5	6	7	8	9	10	11
	6	7	8	9	10	11	12

(a) What is the probability that Emma wins the first time she plays?

(b) Is the game likely to produce a profit or a loss for the school? Justify your answer.

(c) When Ray plays the game he scores 3 with his first spinner. When he adds the score from the other spinner what is the probability that he wins?

(d) When Sally plays the game she scored 6 on the first spinner. What chance does she have of winning when she adds the score on her second spinner?

4   A motorist decides to buy a new car, the list price of which is £14 880. If he sells his old car privately for £4600 and then pays cash for the new car, he is given a discount of $12\frac{1}{2}\%$. However, if he offers his car in part-exchange, it is valued at £5000 and in addition he must make 36 monthly payments of £356. How much will he save if he sells his car privately and pays cash?

5

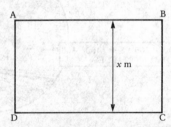

A rectangular table top has a perimeter of 12 m.

(a) Write down, in terms of the width of the table x m, an expression for the surface area of the top of the table.

(b) The area of the top is 6.3 m². Show that $x^2 - 6x + 6.3 = 0$.

(c) Copy and complete the table of values for $y = x^2 - 6x + 6.3$.

x	0	1	1.5	2	3	4	4.5	5	6
y	6.3		−0.45	−1.7	−2.7	−1.7	−0.45	1.3	

(d) Draw the graph of $y = x^2 - 6x + 6.3$ for values of x from 0 to 6. Use $4\,\text{cm} \equiv 1$ unit for x and $2\,\text{cm} \equiv 1$ unit for y.

(e) Use your graph to find an approximate value for the width of the table top.

6

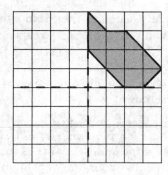

The square tile shown in the sketch has two axes of symmetry as shown.

(a) Complete the shading to show the full pattern.

(b) What fraction of the completed pattern is
   (i) shaded,   (ii) unshaded?

7 For every 16 pupils a school can have 1 teacher, rounded up to the nearest whole number. For example a school with 813 pupils is allowed 50.8 i.e. 51 teachers.

(a) Capital school has 1108 pupils. How many teachers are permitted?

(b) Next year they will have 58 fewer pupils. How many staff must they lose?

8

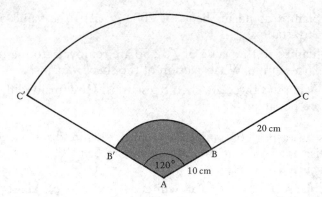

The sketch shows a windscreen wiper which consists of an arm AC and a rubber blade BC. A, B and C are always in a straight line.

(a) If $AB = 10\,\text{cm}$, $BC = 20\,\text{cm}$ and $B'\widehat{A}B = 120°$, find the area of windscreen cleaned by the blade.

(b) How far does the tip of the blade, C, move during each wipe?

223

9   The benefits of a pension scheme are a lump sum payment on retirement equal to $\dfrac{3X}{80}$ of the annual salary, together with an annual pension equal to $\dfrac{X}{80}$ of the annual salary, where X is the number of years worked. Calculate the lump sum and annual pension due to an employee who retires after 37 years' service when earning £15 040 p.a.

10 Universe chocolate is made in rectangular blocks measuring 12 cm by 8 cm × 8 mm, selling at 48 p each.

(a) In order to make more profit, the firm reduces the amount of chocolate in each block by 20%. If the length of the new block remains the same and the width is increased by 10%, find its new thickness, giving your answer in mm correct to one decimal place.

(b) Calculate the original selling price of 1 cm³ of chocolate.

(c) Calculate the new selling price of 1 cm³ of chocolate if the new block is sold for 50 p.

(d) Find the percentage increase, correct to the nearest whole number, in the cost of 1 cm³ of this chocolate.

Revision Paper

25

1   (a) Stamps come in sheets of 200. What is the value of a sheet of 26 p stamps?

(b) Stamps to the value of £32.50 are removed from a new sheet of 26 p stamps. What fraction of the sheet remains?

(c) Aziz buys three attached 8 p stamps. How many different layouts are possible?

2   Lois has a bag containing 6 red discs, 4 white discs and 5 black discs. A disc is chosen at random from the bag. What is the probability that this disc is

(a) black,   (b) white,   (c) blue?

3   A rectangular carpet measures 2.5 m by 4.2 m, each measurement being correct to one decimal place. If the exact length is l m and the exact width is b m use inequalities to indicate the maximum and minimum values for l and b. What is the maximum possible area of the carpet?

4   A soccer league has 20 teams. Every team plays each of the other teams twice, once at home and once away. Games are played on Wednesdays and Saturdays.

   (a) How many league games should be played during the season?

   (b) What is the least number of weeks that the season lasts?

   (c) If two new teams join the league how many extra league games must be played? By how many weeks must the season be extended?

5   (a) If $2646 = 2^x \times 3^y \times 7^z$ find x, y and z.

   (b) If $\dfrac{1}{u} + \dfrac{1}{v} = \dfrac{1}{f}$ find f when $u = 4$ and $v = 3$.

   (c) Put $2^5, 3^4, 4^2$ and 5^2 in ascending order.

6   Sheila thinks her watch is 10 minutes fast whereas it is 7 minutes slow. Relying on her watch she arrives at the station to catch the 8 a.m. train to Manchester, allowing herself 5 minutes to spare. Should she catch her train?

7   Kevin keeps budgerigars. If he puts 3 in each cage he has 1 budgerigar without a cage, but if he puts 4 in each cage he has one cage unused. How many budgerigars and how many cages are there?

8   The grid shows the graph of $y = 3x - 3$.

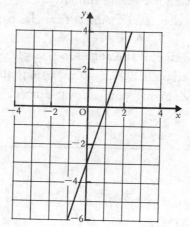

   (a) Copy the graph on to squared paper using 1 cm to represent 1 unit on each axis.

   (b) What is the gradient of the given line?

   (c) On the same grid draw the graph of $y = x + 1$ for values of x from -4 to 3.

   (d) Use your graph to find the values of x and y that satisfy the simultaneous equations $y = 3x - 3$ and $y = x + 1$.

   (e) On your graph, shade the region that satisfies the inequalities $y \geqslant 3x - 3$, $y \leqslant x + 1$, $y \geqslant -2$.

9   The table shows the scores obtaned on an aptitude test (AT) and a mathematics attainment test (MA) by ten Year 11 students.

AT score	11	16	9	12	8	16	12	12	8	10
MA score	29	42	26	30	19	43	35	33	23	28

(a) Using scales of 1 cm to 1 unit for the AT score and 2 cm to 5 units for the MA score draw a scatter diagram to illustrate this information.

(b) Comment on the correlation between the two scores.

(c) Draw a line of best fit.

(d) Sonia scored 38 on the attainment test. What is she likely to score on the aptitude test?

10

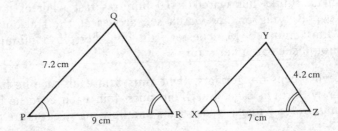

Triangles PQR and XYZ are similar.

(a) Use the properties of similar triangles to find the length of
    (i) QR   (ii) XY.

(b) Prove that one of the angles in triangle XYZ is 90°.

(c) Does the triangle PQR contain a right angle?

(d) Find YX̂Z, giving your answer correct to the nearest tenth of a degree.

Revision Paper

26

1   Study this list of numbers

5, 9, 13, 17, 21, 25, ...

(a) Which of these numbers are prime?

(b) Which of these numbers is the square root of another number in the list?

(c) The numbers form a sequence. Write down the next three numbers in this sequence.

2 The exact area of one face of a cubical block is 20 cm².

   (a) Use your calculator to find, correct to two decimal places, the length of one edge of this cube.

   (b) Find, correct to four significant figures, the volume of the block.

3 In the game of rugby football a line used to be drawn across the width of the field 25 yards from the goal line. In modern rugby it has been replaced by a line 22 metres from the goal line. If $1\ \text{m} \equiv 39.37$ inches and 1 yard $\equiv$ 36 inches, determine whether the line has moved nearer to or further away from, the goal line. By how much has it been moved? Give your answer correct to the nearest inch.

4 (a) Factorise (i) $a^2 - 5a$ (ii) $a^2 + 7a$ (iii) $3a^2b + 2ab^2$.

   (b) Simplify   (i) $\dfrac{5x}{8} + \dfrac{3x}{4}$ (ii) $\dfrac{5x}{8} - \dfrac{3x}{4}$ (iii) $\dfrac{5x}{4} \div \dfrac{3x}{4}$.

5 (a) Solve the inequalities
     (i) $7n + 5 < 19$ (ii) $5n + 3 < n + 15$.

   (b) (i) Write down the smallest whole number value of n that satisfies the inequality $3n + 2 > 11$.

      (ii) Write down the largest whole number value of n that satisfies the inequality $4n + 1 < n + 16$.

6

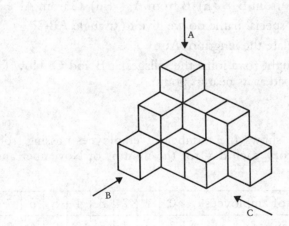

   (a) How many cubes have been used to make this stack?

   (b) Draw what you see by looking at the stack from direction A.

   (c) Draw the view (i) from direction B, (ii) from direction C.

   (d) If each cube has a volume of $1\ \text{cm}^3$ calculate the total area of the stack that is exposed.

   (e) How many separate visible horizontal surfaces does this stack have?

   (f) Does this solid have an axis of symmetry?

7 Ken has a 5 m length of plastic capping. His saw makes a cut 2 mm wide.
   (a) He cuts the capping into four equal lengths. How long is each piece?
   (b) What is the length of each piece if he cuts the capping into ten equal pieces?

8 Draw a diagram to represent the region described by the inequalities $x \geqslant -3$, $x - 2y < 2$, $x + y \leqslant 1$. Scale both axes from -4 to 4.

9
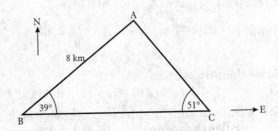

   The diagram shows the position of three villages.
   (a) What is the bearing of
       (i) A from B, (ii) B from A, (iii) C from A?
   (b) What special name do we give to triangle ABC?
   (c) Calculate the length of AC.
   (d) A straight road joins the villages at B and C. How far is A from this road at its nearest point?

10 The table shows the number of employees missing from work at a small factory each day for the months of November and December last year.

Number of employees	0	1	2	3	4	5	6	7	8	9	10
Frequency	3	2	4	5	7	9	4	2	2	0	1

   (a) For how many days was the factory open?
   (b) Illustrate the data with a frequency polygon.
   (c) Find the mean number of staff absent each day.
   (d) Make a cumulative frequency table and then draw a cumulative frequency curve.
   (e) Find the median and interquartile range.

1   Two numbers, M and N, are connected by a formula. To find M, start with N, multiply by 4 and then subtract 3.

(a) Find M when $N = 6$.

(b) Write down a formula for M in terms of N.

(c) Use your formula to find N when $M = 17$.

2   Solve the equations

(a) $3a + 2 = 11$ (b) $5(b + 2) = 25$

(c) $6c + 7 = 3c - 8$ (d) $\dfrac{a}{5} = 6$

(e) $(x + 5)(x - 9) = 0$ (f) $x^2 + 3x - 28 = 0$

3   (a) Find the value of $5000 - 4.78 \times 21^2$.

(b) Rod has £1.80 and Jeff has £2.70. How much must Rod give to Jeff so that Jeff has twice as much as Rod?

4   (a) If I reverse the digits in my age I get my daughter's age. Five years ago I was four times as old as my daughter. How old am I?

(b) What is the smallest whole number which, when divided by 4, 5 and 7, leaves a remainder of 2?

5   By placing a decimal point in the correct position, give the 5 in each of the following numbers the value of 5 hundredths.

$$725, \quad 458, \quad 3865$$

What is the difference between the largest and smallest of these numbers?

6

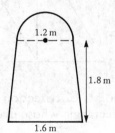

The diagram shows the cross-section of a wall which consists of a trapezium surmounted by a semicircle. The dimensions are shown on the diagram, which is not drawn to scale.

(a) How high is the wall?

(b) Find

     (i) the area of the semicircle,

     (ii) the area of the trapezium,

     (iii) the area of the cross-section.

(c) If the wall is 60 m long find the total amount of material used to build it.

7

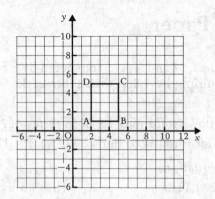

Copy the diagram on to squared paper and show the position of ABCD resulting from

(a) a rotation about A so that the coordinates of B are $(2, -2)$. Label it I. What are the new coordinates of C and D?

(b) a rotation anticlockwise about O through $90°$. Label it II.

(c) a reflection in the line $y = -1$. Label it III.

(d) an enlargement, centre the origin, scale factor 2. Label it IV.

(e) a reflection in the line $y = -x$. Label it V.

8

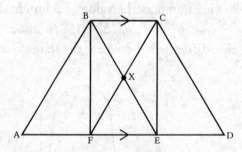

E and F are the points of trisection of the base AD of a trapezium ABCD. BCEF is a rectangle whose diagonals intersect at X. AB = CD.

(a) Name five triangles that are congruent with $\triangle$ABF.

(b) Name three lines that are equal in length to BE.

(c) What type of quadrilateral is BCDE?

(d) Name a triangle that is congruent with FCD.

(e) Name two quadrilaterals that have areas equal to the area of quadrilateral ABCF.

(f) Describe a transformation that will map $\triangle$BFE to
  (i) $\triangle$BFA   (ii) $\triangle$BCE   (iii) $\triangle$CED.

9 The cumulative frequency graph shows the 'life' in hours, of a sample of 500 electric light bulbs.

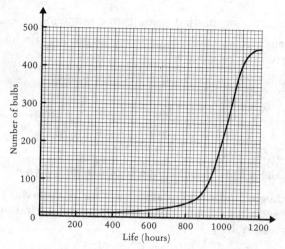

(a) How many bulbs had zero life?

(b) How many bulbs were still working at the end of the test?

(c) For this data find (i) the median, (ii) the upper and lower quartiles, (iii) the interquartile range.

(d) What can you say about the length of the life of these bulbs?

10

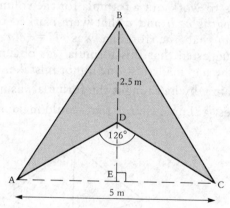

The diagram, which is not drawn to scale, represents a large symmetrical arrow which has been painted on the ground at one end of a runway.

(a) Find DE, DC and BC.

(b) Hence find the perimeter of the arrow, giving your answer correct to the nearest half metre.

(c) Cat's eyes are laid at $\frac{1}{2}$ m intervals along the perimeter. How many cat's eyes are required?

(d) Find the area of the arrow.

231

1. (a) Write down the first seven prime numbers.

   (b) Write down the sequence you get by finding the difference between consecutive prime numbers.

   (c) Find the next two terms in the sequences
   (i) 5, 8, 12, 17, ...,
   (ii) 6, 15, 35, 77, 152, ...

2. (a) If $a = \frac{1}{3}$ and $b = -2$ find the value of
   (i) $6a - 3b$ (ii) $9a^2 - 2b^2$.

   (b) Make q the subject of the formula $p = 3\sqrt{q}$.

3. The straight line with equation $y = mx + c$ passes through the point $(3, 1)$ and is parallel to the line $y = 2x + 5$. Find m and c. Show the line in a sketch.

4. (a) Expand and simplify
   (i) $(3x + 2)(2x - 5)$
   (ii) $(2x - 7)(3x - 4)$
   (iii) $(4x - 3)(4x + 3)$

   (b) Solve the equations   (i) $9 - 4x = 17$ (ii) $\dfrac{5}{y} = 4$.

5. Penny has to work out a formula for the volume of a shape, in terms of the lengths a, b and c that were marked on it. She came to the conclusion that the formula was $V = \frac{2}{3}c(a^2 + b^2 + c)$. Her elder brother suggested that this formula was obviously wrong but suggested that she had made just one minor mistake.

   (a) Explain why he thought the formula was incorrect.

   (b) Suggest a simple change that would make it acceptable.

6.

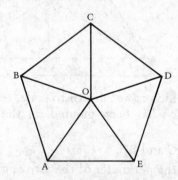

The diagram shows a regular pentagon with centre O.

   (a) What is the order of rotational symmetry of a regular pentagon?

   (b) Find   (i) $C\widehat{O}D$ (ii) $O\widehat{D}C$ (iii) $C\widehat{D}E$.

   (c) Using the given diagram, list four vertices, including C, which form a trapezium.

7

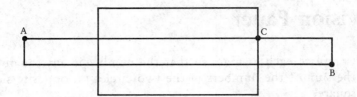

(a) How many different rectangles can you find in this shape?

(b) How many different routes are there from A to B via C without passing through any point in the network more than once?

8

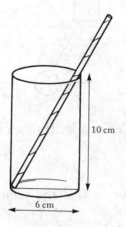

10 cm

6 cm

A straight drinking straw, 20 cm long, rests against the rim of a cylindrical drinking glass such that the greatest possible length of straw is inside the glass. The glass is 10 cm deep and has an internal diameter of 6 cm. What length of straw projects above the rim of the glass?

9 The perimeter of a triangle is 47 cm long.

(a) The longest side is x cm. The shortest side is 7 cm shorter than the longest side and the third side is 4 cm longer than the shortest side. Write down expressions for the length of each side in terms of x.

(b) Form an equation and solve it to find the length of
(i) the longest side,   (ii) the shortest side.

10 Draw x and y axes and scale them from −6 to 6. Shade the region defined by the inequalities.

$$x \leqslant 3, \quad y \leqslant 4 \quad x \geqslant -2, \quad 3x + 2y \geqslant -2.$$

What name describes the shape of this region?

Revision Paper   29

1   Complete each diagram so that the number in any square is equal to
    the sum of the numbers in the two circles on opposite sides of that
    square.

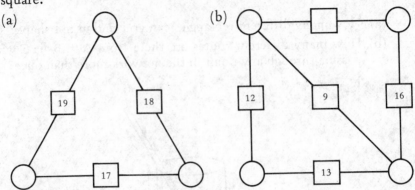

(a)   (b)

2   Without using a calculator write down an approximate value for

    $$\frac{\sqrt{15.8 \times 1.98^2}}{11.62 + 4.81}.$$

    Use your calculator to find the value of this expression correct to
    3 significant figures.

3   In a scientific experiment the time, T seconds, for a reaction to occur
    at $t°C$ is given by the formula $T = t^4 - t^2 + 2$. Find T when
    (a) $t = 3$ (b) $t = -5$.

4   At a school fête they sell 432 raffle tickets numbered 1 to 432. One
    prize is to be awarded. Jo buys tickets numbered 30 to 35 and her
    mother buys tickets numbered 132 to 143.
    (a) What is the probability that
        (i) Jo wins a prize,
        (ii) either Jo or her mother wins the prize?
    (b) How many tickets should they buy between them to be certain
        of winning?

5   (a) A market trader bought 100 videos for £400. When he sold the
        tapes he intended to make a profit of 40%. He sold 75 videos
        at £5.99 each, and, because he wanted to get rid of all of them
        that day, the remainder at £3.99 each. Did he make more than
        40% profit or less than 40% profit? Justify your answer.

    (b) The following week he bought another 100 videos at a 15%
        discount on the price he had previously paid. How much did he
        pay for this batch?

        He sold all of these tapes at the same price and thereby made a
        profit of £110. What was his selling price for each video?

6   The results of the 1992 General Election are given in the table.

Party	Number of seats	Percentage of votes cast	Percentage seats in the House of Commons
Conservatives	336	41.9	51.6
Labour	271	34.5	41.6
Liberal Democrats	20	17.9	3.1
Scottish Nationalists	3	1.9	0.5
Plaid Cymru	4	0.5	0.6
Other	17	3.3	2.6

(a) What majority did the Conservative party have over all other parties?

(b) In a vote, 25 Conservative backbenchers voted against the government, the Liberal Democrats plus 5 of the 'Other' members voted with the government, and of those who failed to vote, 12 were Conservatives, 4 Labour and 1 Scottish Nationalist. What was the result?

7   Peacehaven and Roxley are 20 miles apart. Signposts are placed every mile along the road showing the distance from that signpost to each town.

(a) How many signposts are needed, including the one in Peacehaven and the one in Roxley?

(b) One signpost, showing that it is 11 miles to Peacehaven and 9 miles to Roxley, uses just two digits, namely 1 (twice) and 9. How many of the signposts *between* the two towns use exactly two digits? (Include zeros.)

(c) How many signposts use exactly three digits?

(d) How many times is the digit 2 used altogether?

(e) Which digit is used most frequently? How many times is this?

(f) Each time a digit is replaced it costs 80 p. How much will it cost to replace all the digits on all the signposts?

8   In an experiment the quantities P, D and Q are connected by the formula

$$P = \frac{D}{370(Q \times 10^{-4})}$$

Find P when $D = 30$ and $Q = 7$.

9 Freddy and Maggie are poor school attenders. The probability that Freddy attends school on any one day is $\frac{5}{6}$ and the probability that Maggie attends is $\frac{3}{4}$. Today is Sunday and school is open every day next week.

(a) Who is the more likely to be in school tomorrow, Freddy or Maggie?

(b) What is the probability that Freddy will be absent on Wednesday?

(c) What is the probability that both of them will be absent on Tuesday?

(d) Next Friday, what is the probability that one of them will be absent and one of them will be present?

(e) There are 192 days in the school year. On how many of these days would you expect
(i) both of them to attend,
(ii) both of them to be absent?

10 A swimming pool, with a square base, and of constant depth, has a capacity of 75 m^3. All four sides and the base are tiled.

(a) If the side of the base is x m long, find an expression for the depth of the pool in terms of x.

(b) Show that the total tiled surface, $A \text{ m}^2$, is given by

$$A = x^2 + \frac{300}{x}.$$

(c) Copy and complete the following table:

x	2	3	4	5	6	7	8
A	154		91			92	102

(d) Using a scale of 2 cm for one unit on the x-axis and 1 cm for 10 units on the A-axis, draw a graph to show how A varies with x.

(e) What should be the length of the base to give the minimum amount of tiling? Find the corresponding depth.

Revision Paper   30

1 (a) Express 1058 in prime factors.

(b) A group of pupils pay a total of £529 to go on a trip. If each pupil pays the same amount, and this is a whole number of pounds, how much does each one pay?

2 (a) Bina has a wad of £10 notes that are numbered consecutively from 745375 to 745448. Find their total value.

 (b) The circumference of a circular plate is 80 cm. Find its area.

3 (a) The first five numbers in a sequence are

   5, 9, 17, 29, 45

   (i) Write down the next three numbers in this sequence.
   (ii) Explain why all the numbers in this sequence are odd.

 (b) Another sequence can be obtained by substituting in order $n = 1$, $n = 2$, $n = 3$, etc. in the expression $\frac{n}{2}(n + 3)$. Write down the first six terms of this sequence.

4 (a) A tank holds 2500 litres of petrol. If 1 gallon $\equiv 4.54$ litres, find the capacity of the tank in gallons.

 (b) Barrie, Windsor and Scot are three brothers. Barrie is 4 cm taller than Windsor and Windsor is 8 cm shorter than Scott. The sum of their heights is 477 cm. How tall is Scot?

5 A 'silver' coin is 60% copper, 25% nickel and the rest zinc.

 (a) Give the ratio of copper to nickel to zinc in the form $a:b:c$ in as simple a way as possible.

 (b) To make a given batch of coins 120 kg of copper and 50 kg of nickel are used. How much zinc is needed?

 (c) How much copper is needed to make coins that have a total weight of 120 kg?

6

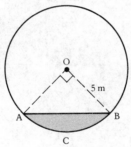

The diagram shows the cross-section of a motorway tunnel through a hillside. The position of the surface of the road, AB, is such that $A\hat{O}B = 90°$ where O is the centre of the circular cross-section.

 (a) Find
   (i) the area of the circle centre O, radius OB,
   (ii) the area of the sector of the circle AOBC,
   (iii) the area of $\triangle AOB$,
   (iv) the area of the cross-section of the tunnel,
   (v) the width of the road surface AB.

 (b) If the tunnel is 500 m long, find the amount of space inside the tunnel.

7   Mrs Boaz pays £1.45 for 3 oranges and 2 grapefruit while Mr Carter pays £2.75 for 5 oranges and 4 grapefruit. If an orange costs x p and a grapefruit costs y p write down two equations in x and y. Solve these equations to find the cost of one grapefruit.

8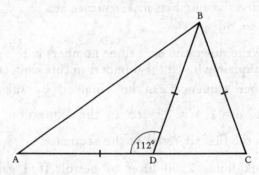

In the diagram $AD = BD = BC$. Find the size of
(a) $B\widehat{A}D$ (b) $B\widehat{D}C$ (c) $C\widehat{B}D$.

9   A ship sails 60 nautical miles on a bearing of 125°. It then changes course and sails 160 nautical miles on a bearing of 040°.
(a) Draw a scale drawing using 1 cm to represent 6 nautical miles.
(b) Find the distance and bearing of the ship from its starting point.

10   The nth term of a sequence (u_n) is given by $u_n = u_{n-1} - u_{n-2}$. If $u_1 = 1$ and $u_2 = 3$, find the next six terms. Can you see a pattern that enables you to write down additional terms?

Answers

Part 1: Exercises

Number Work

1 (a) 11, 13   (b) 25, 30
   (c) 49, 64   (d) 20, −24
   (e) 0.0001, 0.000 01
   (f) 128, 256

2 (a) −8, −4, 1, 3, 5
   (b) 0.3, 0.33, $\frac{1}{3}$, $\frac{2}{5}$
   (c) $\frac{1}{4}$, $\frac{1}{3}$, $\frac{5}{12}$, $\frac{1}{2}$
   (d) 3.04, 3.14, 3.41, 3.411

3 (a) $10\frac{1}{8}$ (b) $\frac{3}{4}$ (c) 1
   (d) 8   (e) 24   (f) $3\frac{3}{4}$

4 (a) 6.14   (b) 2.82
   (c) 0.136   (d) 4
   (e) 2.64   (f) 3.6

5 (a) 200   (b) 2
   (c) 36   (d) 8

6 (a) 594   (b) 0.072   (c) 39.6

7 (a) (i) 9200   (ii) 9220
     (iii) 9217.79
   (b) (i) 100   (ii) 95.7
     (iii) 95.72
   (c) (i) 400   (ii) 416
     (iii) 416.35

8 (a) 2.24   (b) 6.93
   (c) 0.438   (d) 1.15
   (e) 7.39   (f) 4.64

9 (a) 6   (b) 7   (c) 14
   (d) 18   (e) 15   (f) 54

10 (a) 84   (b) 35   (c) 112
   (d) 72   (e) 132   (f) 175

11 (a) $5\frac{1}{2} < 5.55$ (b) $0.78 > 0.69$
   (c) $-0.042 > -0.12$
   (d) $-0.7 > -0.81$
   (e) $3\frac{3}{8} = 3.375$ (f) $-1.4 < 1\frac{2}{5}$

12 (a) $3\frac{1}{8}(3.125)$, $\frac{377}{120}(3.141\,66\ldots)$,
     3.141 88, $\left(\frac{39}{22}\right)^2 (3.142\,56\ldots)$,
     $\sqrt{10}\,(3.162\,277\ldots)$
   (b) $\frac{377}{120}$

13 (a) −8   (b) −14   (c) 11
   (d) −3   (e) 12   (f) −5
   (g) 32   (h) 16   (i) 24
   (j) −2

14 (a) (i) 1, 19, 31   (ii) 19, 31
   (b) 3, 6, 9, 12
   (c) 46, 64

15 (a) $\frac{17}{32}$ (b) $\frac{7}{27}$ (c) $\frac{13}{60}$
   (d) $1\frac{11}{12}$ (e) $\frac{7}{12}$ (f) $\frac{5}{12}$

16 (a) 3, 11   (b) 5, 19

17 (a) 10.8   (b) 0.21
   (c) 10   (d) 67.05
   (e) 46.8   (f) 42.84
   (g) 12.213

18 $\frac{12}{5}, \frac{5}{8}, \frac{13}{4}$

19 (a) $2 + 3.3$ (b) 5×2.5
   (c) 8.2 and 4
   (d) $\frac{3}{5}$ (or any other acceptable
     answers)

20 (a) $\frac{8}{9}$ (b) $\frac{4}{45}$ (c) $\frac{30}{11}$
   (d) $\frac{3}{110}$

21 (a) 11, 17   (b) 11, 29
   (c) 7, 31   (d) 7, 61

22 (a) No
   (b) (i) 4, 16, 36   (ii) 9, 36
   (c) 49, 64
   (d)

23 (a) $2n$ is even, therefore $2n − 1$
     is odd
   (b) $2n$ (c) $2n + 1$
   (d) $6n$; $6n$ is always exactly
     divisible by 6

24

9	2	10
8	7	6
4	12	5

25

10	3	14
13	9	5
4	15	8

26 (a) 14, 21   (b) 32, 24
   (c) 4.5, 1   (d) 440, 600
   (e) 14, 21, 28   (f) 90, 144, 198

27 $x = 5$, $y = 2$, $z = 1$

28 (a) (i) 2 (ii) 243
    (iii) $\frac{1}{9}$ (iv) 64
    (b) (i) the same (ii) 3^7

29 £3.57

30 (a) (i) $3.5 \leqslant l < 4.5$
    (ii) $2.5 \leqslant b < 3.5$
    (b) (i) 8.75
    (ii) Just less than 15.75

31 3

32 6.75

33 4

34 9.3×10^7

35 6.7×10^7

36 7.7×10^8

37 5.87×10^9

38 (a) B (b) D
    (c) 1 : 3.5 (d) 107 min

39 (a) 1 6 15 20 15 6 1
        1 7 21 35 35 21 7 1
    (b) 1, 2, 4, 8, 16, 32, 64, 128
    (c) 2^0, 2^1, 2^2, 2^3, 2^4, 2^5, 2^6, 2^7
    (d) (i) 2^{11} (ii) 2^{20}

40 (a)

(b)

Design number	Number of tiles required
1	1
2	4
3	9
4	16
5	25

(c) (i) 64 (ii) 144

41 30 800

42 (a) £8800 (b) £2000
    (c) £1200

43 (a) (i) 29 30 (ii) 16 17
            34 35   21 22
    (b) (i) 100 (ii) No such square
    (c) No
    (d) (i) 24, 25, 29, 30
        (ii) 31, 32, 36, 37
    (e) (i) 42 (ii) 0
    (f) (i) 62, 0 (ii) 14, 0
        (iii) 58, 0
    (g) $2(n + 3)$, 0

44 $\frac{3}{5}$

45 8, 21

Sequences

1 (a) 14, 17 (b) 30, 35
   (c) 35, 43 (d) 22, 26
   (e) −10, −12 (f) 0, −5
   (g) 25, 36 (h) 27, 38
   (i) $\frac{5}{6}, \frac{6}{7}$ (j) 15, 21
   (k) $1 + 3 + 5 + 7 + 9$,
       $1 + 3 + 5 + 7 + 9 + 11$

2 (a) $3n - 1$ (b) $5(n + 1)$
   (c) $8n - 5$ or $5n + 5$
   (d) $4n + 2$ (e) $-2n$
   (f) $5(5 - n)$ (g) n^2
       or $25 - 5n$ (h) $n^2 + 2$
   (i) $\dfrac{n}{n + 1}$

3 (a) (5, 13) (b) (10, 23)
   (c) $(n, 2n + 3)$

4 (a) (i) 4 (ii) 12 (iii) 24
   (b) (i) 40 (ii) 60
       (iii) $2n(n + 1)$

5 (a) 15, 21, 28, 36 (b) 55
   (c) 4, 16, 36, 64
   (d) 100, 144, $(2n)^2$ i.e. $4n^2$

6 (a) 9, 9.5
   (b) 12, 4, 8, 6, 7, 6.5, ...

7 (a) (i) 10 (ii) 12 (iii) 18
   (b) $2n + 2$ (c) 10
   (d) No, the number of chairs used
       is always even.

8 (a) (i) 5   (ii) 9   (iii) 13
   (b) (i) 41
        (ii) $4n + 1$, i.e. $4(n - 1) + 5$
   (c) 15
9 (a)

5   6

   (b)

Diagram number	1	2	3	4	5	6
Number of black tiles	1	3	6	10	15	21
Number of white tiles	8	12	16	20	24	28

   (c) (i) 36   (ii) 40
   (d) $b = \dfrac{n}{2}(n + 1)$, $w = 4(n + 1)$
   (e) (i) 78   (ii) 44
   (f) Yes, if $n = 8$.
10 (a) 7, 11, 13, 17, 19, 23
   (b) e.g. 2, 3, 5, 8, 12, 17, adding 1 more each time. (Other sequences are possible.)
11 (a) (i) 56, 72
        (ii) The first term is even and the difference between consecutive terms is always even.
   (b) 1, 3, 6, 10, 15, 21, $n(n + 1)$
12 (a) and (b)

Pattern number	1	2	3	4	5	6
Number of black tiles	1	1	9	9	25	25
Number of white tiles	0	4	4	16	16	36
Total number of tiles	1	5	13	25	41	61

   (c) Yes
   (d) (i) $7^2 + 6^2$ (ii) $10^2 + 9^2$
   (e) $n^2 + (n - 1)^2 = 2n^2 - 2n + 1$
   (f) 12

Basic Algebra   3

1 (a) $7x$ 2 (a) 0   (b) $-2x$
   (b) cannot simplify   (c) cannot simplify
   (c) $2a + b$ (d) $-4a$ (e) $3x$
   (d) cannot simplify   (f) $4a$
   (e) x^2 (f) $3b - a$

3 (a) $11a$ (b) $12a$
    (c) cannot simplify   (d) b
4 (a) $3x^2 - x - 2$
    (b) $7a^2 + 6a + 2$
    (c) $x^2 + 36$
    (d) $4b^2 - 3a - 5$
5 (a) $6a^2$ (b) $5ab$
    (c) $12x^2$ (d) $-6a^2$
    (e) $-8x^2$ (f) $-10x^2$
6 (a) $10x + 15$ (b) $20a - 8$
    (c) $15x - 6$ (d) $21 + 14a$
    (e) $20 - 12a$ (f) $5a^2 + 15a$
7 (a) $7x + 15$ (b) $7a + 22$
    (c) $6x + 36$ (d) $8a + 19$
8 (a) $3a + 16$ (b) $11x - 13$
    (c) $x + 8$ (d) $-a + 27$
9 (a) $x^2 + 10x$ (b) $4a - a^2$
    (c) $x^2 + 3x - 5$ (d) $2x^2 + 2x$
    (e) $2a^2 - 13a$ (f) $4x^2 + 5x$
10 (a) $2x^2 + x$ (b) $a^2 + 3a$
    (c) $3x^2 - 21x$ (d) $a^2 - 8a$
11 (a) $x^2 + 5x + 6$
    (b) $x^2 + 11x + 28$
    (c) $x^2 + 6x + 5$
    (d) $x^2 + 8x + 12$
12 (a) $x^2 - 7x + 12$
    (b) $x^2 - 11x + 30$
    (c) $x^2 - 13x + 30$
    (d) $x^2 - 10x + 9$
13 (a) $x^2 + 4x - 21$
    (b) $x^2 + 5x - 36$
    (c) $x^2 + 2x - 15$
    (d) $x^2 - 3x - 70$
14 (a) $a^2 - 16$
    (b) $x^2 - 49$
    (c) $a^2 + 10a + 25$
    (d) $x^2 - 8x + 16$
15 (a) $4(x + 2)$ (b) $3(3a + 2)$
    (c) $5(t + 2)$ (d) $3(a - 2)$
    (e) $5(2 - a)$ (f) $4(3x - 4)$
16 (a) $x(x + 7)$ (b) $x(x + 12)$
    (c) $3(a^2 + 1)$ (d) $a(5a - 1)$
    (e) $2a(2a - 1)$ (f) $6x(x - 2)$
17 (a) 5 (b) 3 (c) 4
    (d) 15 (e) 12 (f) 15

18 (a) 3 (b) 3 (c) 5
    (d) 3 (e) 8 (f) 2
19 (a) 4 (b) 3 (c) $5\frac{1}{2}$
    (d) $2\frac{1}{2}$ (e) $4\frac{1}{3}$ (f) $1\frac{4}{5}$
20 (a) 9 (b) 3 (c) -2
    (d) -3 (e) -5 (f) 11
    (g) 0 (h) 1
21 (a) 6 (b) 15 (c) 10
    (d) -8 (e) -15 (f) 6
22 (a) 1 (b) 13
    (c) 7 (d) 7
23 (a) 8 (b) $-4\frac{1}{2}$
    (c) 16 (d) 5
24 (a) $\frac{1}{4}$ (b) $\frac{1}{2}$
    (c) $\frac{7}{10}$ (d) $\frac{1}{5}$
25 (a) -13 (b) 16
26 (a) 6 (b) 3
27 (a) $x^2 + 9x + 20$
    (b) $a^2 + 10a + 21$
    (c) $x^2 - 10x + 24$
    (d) $b^2 - 7b + 10$
    (e) $x^2 - 4x - 21$
    (f) $x^2 + x - 30$
    (g) $40 - 13c + c^2$
    (h) $y^2 - 7y + 12$
28 (a) $2x^2 + 13x + 6$
    (b) $3x^2 + 12x + 9$
    (c) $4x^2 - 13x - 35$
    (d) $5x^2 - 18x - 8$
    (e) $7x^2 + 37x - 30$
    (f) $3x^2 - 3x - 18$
    (g) $4x^2 - 27x + 18$
    (h) $9x^2 - 43x + 28$
29 (a) $12x^2 + 29x + 14$
    (b) $42x^2 + 51x + 15$
    (c) $24x^2 - 71x + 35$
    (d) $20x^2 - 32x + 3$
    (e) $10x^2 - 3x - 4$
    (f) $18x^2 - 2$
    (g) $16x^2 - 9$
    (h) $25x^2 - 10x - 8$

Simultaneous Linear Equations   4

1   $x = 3, \ y = 2$ 2 $x = 5, \ y = 2$
3   $x = 3, \ y = 4$ 4 $x = 3, \ y = 2$
5   $x = 3, \ y = -2$ 6 $x = 4, \ y = -1$
7   $x = 5, \ y = 1$ 8 $x = 2, \ y = -1$
9   $x = 1, \ y = -4$ 10 $x = 4, \ y = 3$
11   $x = -3, \ y = 4$ 12 $x = 2, \ y = 2$
13   7 years
14   (a) 16p   (b) 8p   (c) 64p

15   Peter is 9 years old and his father is 31 years old
16   90p
17   10 and 8
18   Lime 60p, orange 50p
19   £2.55
20   (a) 26p   (b) 20p

Formulas

1 (a) 13   (b) 18   (c) 72
   (d) 25   (e) 0   (f) 7
   (g) 25   (h) 5   (i) 6
   (j) $\frac{1}{2}$ (k) 2   (l) 11

2 (a) 20   (b) 7   (c) 3

3 (a) 21   (b) 4   (c) 9

4 (a) 24   (b) 9

5 (a) £14   (b) £34   (c) £39

6 (a) £15   (b) (i) £20   (ii) £190

7 (a) £194   (b) 44

8 (a) £900   (b) 8000 miles

9 (a) (i) 720   (ii) 180
   (b) 60

10 $s = 3n - 3$

11 $s = 3n + 6$

12 $s = 3n$

13 (a) $D = n - 3$
    (b) (i) 4   (ii) 15

14 (a) (i) £24   (ii) £80   (iii) £8p
    (b) (i) £20   (ii) £75   (iii) £5q
    (c) $C = 8p + 5q$

15 (a) (i) £1   (ii) £2.50   (iii) $£\frac{x}{2}$
    (b) (i) £6   (ii) £10.50   (iii) $£\frac{3y}{2}$
    (c) $C = \frac{x}{2} + \frac{3y}{2}$ or $C = \frac{1}{2}(x + 3y)$

16 (a) $b = a - c$ (b) $b = \frac{A}{h}$
    (c) $c = y - mx$ (d) $R = \frac{C}{2\pi}$
    (e) $\pi = \frac{C}{D}$ (f) $v = \frac{12}{p}$
    (g) $b = \frac{v}{ac}$ (h) $h = \frac{3v}{\pi r^2}$
    (i) $\pi = \frac{3v}{4r^3}$ (j) $b = ax - y$

17 (a) 5 cm   (b) 8 cm

18 (a) 5 cm   (b) 8 cm²

19 (a) $F = 2(C + 15)$ (b) -30
    (c) To find C, subtract 15 from half the value of F.
    (d) -22
    (e) 60°F, 61°F or 62°F.

Percentages

1 (a) 50%   (b) 80%
   (c) 75%   (d) 35%
   (e) 68%   (f) 225%
   (g) 26%   (h) 174%

2 (a) $\frac{3}{10}$ (b) $\frac{3}{5}$ (c) $\frac{1}{4}$
   (d) $\frac{9}{20}$ (e) $\frac{3}{2}$ (f) $\frac{7}{4}$
   (g) $\frac{27}{40}$ (h) $\frac{1}{3}$

3 (a) 50%   (b) 40%   (c) 32%
   (d) $33\frac{1}{3}$%   (e) $12\frac{1}{2}$%   (f) 40%

4 (a) 20p   (b) 2.4 m   (c) 6 litres
   (d) £6   (e) 90p   (f) 42 kg

5 (a) £19.80   (b) £90

6 £8.16

7 £15.60

8 1.38 kg

9 1800

10 £1.79 (to nearest penny)

11 (a) £67 680   (b) £7311.60
    (c) £153 752

12 £68.25

13 £550

14 (a) £164.50   (b) £12.93
    (c) £64.63   (d) £61.10

15 (a) £60.60   (b) £3.24
    (c) £32.76   (d) £297.60

16 £41.71

17 £52.80

18 £74.55

19 (a) £940
    (b) Speedstore by £29

20 Denham's by 25p

21 (a) 35 217   (b) 50 310
    (c) 1528   (d) Aplin by 2155

22 (a) £240, £300, £120
    (b) (i) $1\frac{1}{2}$ (ii) 3   (iii) 40

23 £2160, £3540, 5% plus a car

24 £2703.60
    (a) £2458.80   (b) £614.70

25 (a) £55   (b) £60
    (c) £44   (d) £22
    (e) £99, £33   (f) £59.40

Parallel Lines, Triangles and Quadrilaterals 7

1   $a = 128°$, $b = 78°$, $c = 50°$
2   $d = 100°$
3   $e = 53°$, $f = 64°$
4   $g = 72°$, $h = 36°$, $i = 108°$,
    $j = 36°$
5   $k = 25°$, $l = 48°$
6   $m = 105°$, $n = 75°$, $p = 75°$
7   $q = 74°$, $r = 38°$, $s = 112°$,
    $t = 106°$
8   $u = 18°$
9   $v = 115°$, $w = 37°$
10   $x = 109°$, $y = 55°$, $z = 58°$
11   $a = 82°$, $b = 37°$, $c = 61°$

12   $d = 56°$, $e = 84°$, $f = 40°$
13   $x = 60°$, $2x = 120°$, $3x = 180°$
14   $y = 45°$, $2y = 90°$, $5y = 225°$
15   $z = 83°$
16   $x = 45°$
17   $y = 107°$
18   $z = 117°$
19   $a = 37°$, $b = 106°$, $c = 74°$,
    $d = 32°$
20   $e = 82°$, $f = 44°$, $g = 104°$
21   $h = 57°$, $i = 33°$, $j = 33°$
22   $k = 50°$, $l = 50°$, $m = 130°$

Polygons, Tiles and Tessellations 8

1   Any of the broken lines; 5

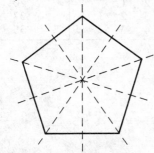

2   $v = 45°$, $w = 67\frac{1}{2}°$, $x = 90°$,
    $y = 45°$, $z = 135°$
3   $x = 120°$, $y = 114°$
4   $p = 126°$, $q = 108°$, $r = 54°$
5   (a) $36°$ (b) $144°$
6   (a) $24°$ (b) $156°$
7   (a) $150°$ (b) 12
8   (a) $20°$ (b) 18
9   (a) Yes   (b) Yes   (c) No
    (d) Yes
10   (a) Yes   (b) No   (c) Yes
     (d) No
11   $100°$
12   $125°$, No
13   (a) $60°$
     (b) (i) $120°$ (ii) $30°$ (iii) $30°$
        (iv) $90°$ (v) $60°$

14   (a) $72°$
     (b) (i) $108°$ (ii) $36°$
        (iii) $72°$ (iv) $36°$
15   (a) (i) $60°$ (ii) $120°$
     (b) (i) $60°$ (ii) $60°$
     (c) equilateral
     (d) (i) Because $\widehat{EBG} = \widehat{BEG} = 60°$
        (ii) equilateral
16   (a) $90°$ (b) $108°$ (c) $162°$
17   (a) $\widehat{AFE} = \widehat{BCD} = 90°$, the other
       angles are $135°$
     (b) 2   (c) $300\,\text{cm}^2$
     (d) $68.3\,\text{cm}$
     (e) (i) D   (ii) B
18   (a) 6   (b) $60°$
     (c) equilateral   (d) $120°$
     (e) $4.33\,\text{cm}$
     (f) (i) $10.83\,\text{cm}^2$ (ii) $65.0\,\text{cm}^2$
     (g) $13.5\,\text{cm}^2$
19   (a) trapezium, one
     (b) $135°$
     (c)   No

(d) 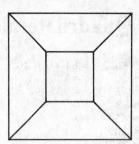 2500 cm²

(e) $y = 2x$

20 (a) 90°
   (b) (i) 360°   (ii) 30°
   (c) a square
   (d) a trapezium
   (e) yes, two

21 (a)

Number of sides (n)	Number of diagonals that can be drawn from $A(d)$	Number of new diagonals that can be drawn from							Total number of diagonals (D)
		B	C	D	E	F	G	H	
3	0								0
4	1	1							2
5	2	2	1						5
6	3	3	2	1					9
7	4	4	3	2	1				14
8	5	5	4	3	2	1			20
9	6	6	5	4	3	2	1		27
10	7	7	6	5	4	3	2	1	35

(b) { (rows 9 and 10)

(c) (i) $\dfrac{n}{2}d$ (ii) $\dfrac{n}{2}(n-3)$

22 120°, 6

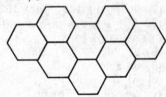

23 (a) pentagon   (b) rhombus
   (c) (i) 108°   (ii) 36°   (iii) 144°

24 (a)

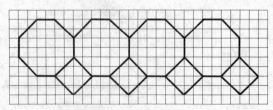

(b) (i) 8 cm²   (ii) 28 cm²
   (c) 90°

(d) 135°, 135°
(e) 135°
(f) No
(g)

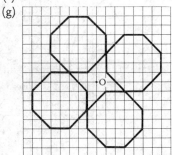

25 (a)

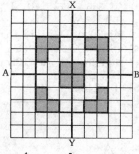

(b) (i) $\frac{4}{9}$ (ii) $\frac{5}{9}$
(c) $\frac{5}{9}$
(d) (i) 384   (ii) 54   (iii) 8
    (iv) £129.60   (v) 48

Indices   9

1 (a) a^7 (b) a^{11} (c) x^5
   (d) x^{19} (e) a^6 (f) x^9

2 (a) a^3 (b) x (c) b
   (d) t^3 (e) 1   (f) x^4

3 (a) $\frac{1}{x^2}$ (b) $\frac{1}{x^3}$ (c) $\frac{1}{a^2}$
   (d) $\frac{1}{b}$ (e) $\frac{1}{a}$ (f) 1

4 (a) a (b) x^4 (c) 1
   (d) a^2 (e) a^2 (f) b^4

5 (a) $\frac{1}{a}$ (b) $\frac{1}{b^2}$ (c) $\frac{1}{x}$
   (d) $\frac{1}{x}$ (e) 1   (f) $\frac{1}{a^5}$

6 (a) $6a^5$ (b) $6x^7$ (c) $10b^4$
   (d) $12a^6$ (e) $18x^5$ (f) $15x^7$

7 (a) $6a^2b^3$ (b) $8a^4b^4$
   (c) $16a^3b^2$ (d) $6a^4b^3$
   (e) $5a^2b^3$ (f) $6a^2b^4$

8 (a) 2   (b) 2   (c) $2a$
   (d) $4b$ (e) $5a$ (f) $2a^2$

9 (a) $4a$ (b) $3b$ (c) $3ab$
   (d) $2b$ (e) $3a^2b$ (f) $3a^2b^2$

10 (a) 8   (b) 27   (c) $\frac{1}{4}$
   (d) $\frac{4}{9}$ (e) 32   (f) 81
   (g) 1   (h) $\frac{9}{4}$

11 (a) $\frac{1}{2}$ (b) $\frac{1}{9}$ (c) $\frac{1}{4}$
   (d) $\frac{1}{4}$ (e) $\frac{1}{27}$ (f) $\frac{1}{25}$
   (g) 1   (h) $\frac{1}{7}$

12 (a) 2   (b) 3   (c) 4
   (d) 6   (e) $\frac{5}{2}$ (f) $\frac{3}{7}$
   (g) $\frac{2}{3}$ (h) $\frac{5}{3}$

Scale Drawings and Loci   10

1 (a) 1 m   (b) 4 m by 3 m
   (c) (i) 3 cm by 2.5 cm
       (ii) 7.5 cm²
2 (a) 500 m   (b) 15 km
   (c) 375 m   (d) 10 cm
3 (a) 10 cm   (b) 9 cm
   (c) 6 cm

4 (a) 7.07 km   (b) 11 km
5 (a) 20 m   (b) 170 m
   (c) (i) 80 m   (ii) 176 m
6 PQ = 8.14 cm, $\widehat{PQR}$ = 80.4°
7 (a) 70.7 cm   (b) 122 cm
   (c) 178.5 cm

8 (a) (i) 5 m × 4 m   (ii) 4.3 m × 4 m
    (iii) 3.8 m × 3.2 m
  (b) (i) 20 m^2 (ii) 12.16 m^2
  (c) £400   (d) £5
9 (a) 8.59 cm   (b) 12.7 cm
  (c) 12.7 cm
10 (b) (i) 3.46 m   (ii) 2 m
   (c)

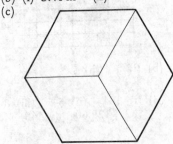

11 AS = 2.46 km, BS = 1.38 km
12 1040 m, 011°
13 (a) 370 m, 065°
    (b) 370 m, 245°
14 8.49 km, 046°
15 (a) a circle, centre A, radius 10 cm
    (b) a circle, centre D, radius 8 cm
    (c) a circle, centre E, radius 5 cm
    (d) a circle, centre C, radius 5 cm

16

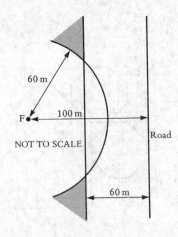

60 m

F   100 m

NOT TO SCALE

Road

60 m

17

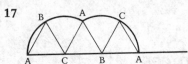

The locus of A is indicated
by the curved line

18 (a) 4.5 km, 058°
    (b) (i) 220°   (ii) 35 km/h

Pythagoras' Theorem   11

1 (a) 5 cm   (b) 6 cm
  (c) 2 cm   (d) 2.1 cm
  (e) 55 cm   (f) 5 cm
  (g) 9.6 cm   (h) 3.14 cm
  (i) 15.65 cm   (j) 21.96 cm
2 (a) 6.10 cm   (b) 12 cm
3 (a) 13.44 cm   (b) 16.86 cm
  (c) 9.79 cm   (d) 45.69 cm
4 35.36 cm
5 (a) (i) x^2 (ii) $4x^2$
  (b) $5x^2 = 50^2$, BC = 22.36 cm
  (c) 1000 cm^2
6 (a) 14.14 cm   (b) 17.32 cm
7 36.4 cm
8 (a) 7.60 m   (b) 7.85 m

9 127 m
10 114 yards
11 20 m
12 8.062 m, 7.483 m
13 586.9 m
14 383 mm
15 (a) 67.22 m   (b) 405 cm^3
   (c) 16 200 cm^3
16 9 cm
17 24 cm
18 (a) 5 m
   (b) 18 m
   (c) 26 m
19 15.9 m
20 22.4 cm by 11.2 cm

Congruency and Similarity **12**

1 Yes   2 Yes   3 No
4 Yes   5 C, E, G   6 A, C, E
7 (a) 3 cm   (b) 6 cm
8 (a) 6 cm   (b) 12 cm   (c) 9 cm
9 (a) 12.5 cm   (b) 16 cm
10 (a) 6 cm   (b) 11 cm
11 (a) (i) 8   (ii) 27
     (b) 1, 19
12 (a) (i) $2\frac{1}{2}$ cm, $1\frac{1}{2}$ cm
       (ii) 10 cm, 6 cm
     (b) A: $4\frac{1}{2}$ cm^2, B: 18 cm^2,
       C: 72 cm^2
     (c) 4 times as much

13 (a) (i) $1\frac{1}{2}$ m   (ii) $4\frac{1}{2}$ m
     (b) (i) 2 m   (ii) 6 m
     (c) (i) $\frac{3}{4}$ m^2 (ii) 3 m^2
       (iii) $\frac{27}{4}$ m^2
     (d) (i) $1\frac{1}{2}$ m^3 (ii) 12 m^3
       (iii) $40\frac{1}{2}$ m^3
     (e) 1 : 8 : 27
14 The 750 g can costs 0.072p per
     gram, which is the cheapest per
     gram
15 (a) 200 g   (b) 50 g
16 All ingredients are doubled
     (actually ratio is 49 : 100)
17 (a) 2 : 3   (b) 4 : 9   (c) 8 : 27

The Straight Line **13**

1 (a) A(2, 2), B(10, 6), C(2, −2),
       D(5, 2), E(−5, 9), F(3, 4),
       G(6, −2), H(9, −6), I(−5, −5),
       J(4, −5) K(−7, −3), L(−7, 6)
     (b) (i) $\frac{1}{2}$ (ii) $\frac{4}{3}$ (iii) $-\frac{5}{8}$
       (iv) $-\frac{4}{3}$ (v) 0   (vi) infinite
2 (a) rectangle   (b) trapezium
     (c) parallelogram   (i) $\frac{2}{5}$ (ii) $\frac{2}{5}$
3 (a) (i) $\frac{1}{2}$ (ii) (0, 2)
     (b) (i) −1   (ii) (0, 5)
     (c) (i) −2   (ii) (0, −6)
     (d) (i) $\frac{3}{5}$ (ii) (0, −3)
4 (a) (i) 2   (ii) (0, 6)
     (b) (i) 3   (ii) (0, −7)
     (c) (i) −5   (ii) (0, 2)
     (d) (i) $-\frac{1}{2}$ (ii) (0, 3)
     (e) (i) −1   (ii) (0, 5)
     (f) (i) −3   (ii) (0, 4)
5 (a) $y = 4x + 5$ (b) $y = -3x + 2$
     (c) $y = \frac{1}{2}x - 4$ (d) $y = -\frac{3}{2}x + \frac{1}{2}$
6 (c) (ii) D(−4, −4)   (iii) E(1, 1)
     (d) (i) two   (ii) rhombus
     (e) (i) 4   (ii) $\frac{1}{4}$
7 (c) (ii) D(5, −2)   (iii) $(1\frac{1}{2}, 1\frac{1}{2})$
     (d) (i) 1   (ii) −1
8 (c) (ii) D(−2, −5)   (iii) E(2, 2)
     (d) (i) $\frac{7}{4}$ (ii) $-\frac{7}{4}$

9 (a)

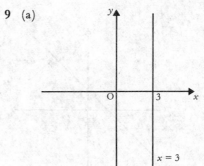

(b)

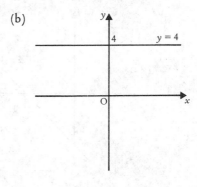

(c)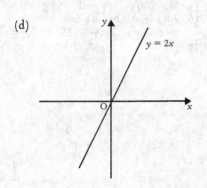

(d)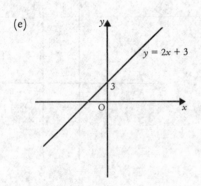

(e)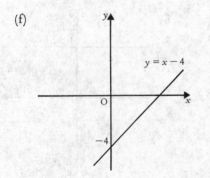

(f)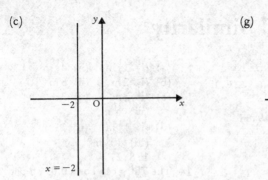

(g)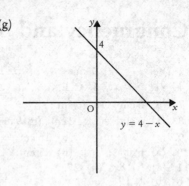

(h)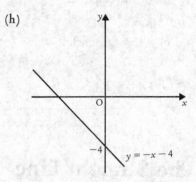

10 (a)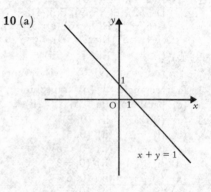

(b)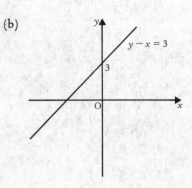

(c)

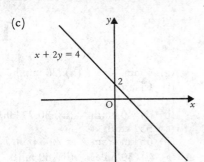

$x + 2y = 4$

(g)

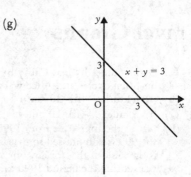

$x + y = 3$

(h)

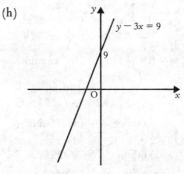

$y - 3x = 9$

(d)

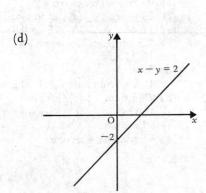

$x - y = 2$

(e)

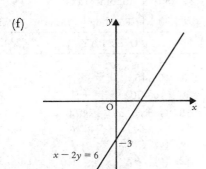

$3x + y = 6$

(f)

$x - 2y = 6$

11 (a) C   (b) B   (c) D
     (d) A

12 (b) (i) 31   (ii) 74   (iii) 10
     (iv) 70

13 (a) $x = \frac{6}{5},\ y = \frac{6}{5}$
     (b) $x = -\frac{1}{2},\ y = -2\frac{1}{2}$
     (c) $x = \frac{3}{2},\ y = \frac{3}{2}$
     (d) $x = 2.6\ (2\frac{4}{7}),\ y = 1.4\ (1\frac{3}{7})$
     (e) $x = 4\frac{1}{2},\ y = -1$
     (f) $x = 4,\ y = -3$
     (g) $x = 1\frac{1}{3},\ y = 3\frac{1}{3}$
     (h) $x = -2.5\,(-2\frac{6}{11})$,
        $y = -0.9\,(-\frac{10}{11})$

14 (a) Floorcraft £14, Westgrove £16
     (b) 6.4 m²
     (c) (i) Floorcraft   (ii) Westgrove
     (d) 6   (e) 5

15 (a) 0.055, 20   (b) 5.5 p
     (c) £20

16 (a) (i)

x	0	50	100	150	200
C	10	30	50	70	90

     (iii) (1) £14   (2) £64

     (b) (i)

x	0	25	100	125	175
B	25	32.5	55	62.5	77.5

     (c) 150 km
     (d) Smith & Son, £3

251

Travel Graphs   14

1 (a) Derek comes by car, Cathy by bus, Ben cycles and Alice walks
   (b) (i) 6 km/h   (ii) 30 km/h

2 (a) (i) 5 miles   (ii) 10 miles
   (b) No — the time scale from 1995 to 1999 is compressed so that it is the same as that for any one year during the period 1990 to 1995

3 (a) (i) 5.04   (ii) $\frac{1}{2}$ km
      (iii) 5 min   (iv) 6 km/h
   (b) 6 min
   (c) (i) $7\frac{1}{2}$ km   (ii) 15 min
      (iii) 30 km/h
   (d) (i) 5.34   (ii) 30 min
      (iii) $8\frac{1}{2}$ km   (iv) 17 km/h

4 (a) $2\frac{1}{4}$ miles   (b) 10 min
   (c) $\frac{1}{4}$ mile   (d) $1\frac{1}{2}$ m.p.h., No
   (e) 4 min   (f) 2 miles

   (g) 6 min   (h) 20 m.p.h.
   (i) $6\frac{3}{4}$ m.p.h.

5 (a) 3.54
   (b) (i) 40 km/h   (ii) 30.77 km/h
   (c) $53\frac{1}{3}$ km/h
   (d) 65 km from A at 2.03 p.m.

6 (a) (i) 30 miles   (ii) 80 miles
   (b) (i) 8.40   (ii) 9.40
   (c) 10 min   (d) 45 m.p.h.
   (e) 9 a.m., 40 miles from A
   (f) 19 miles   (g) 52 m.p.h.

7 (a) 11.46 a.m.   (b) 15 km/h
   (c) 7.3 km from Elmwood at 10.14 a.m.
   (d) 2 km

8 (a) 11 km from Atley at 1.50 p.m.
   (b) 2.45 p.m.   (c) 5.75 km

9 (a) 160 m   (b) Richard
   (c) 82 seconds
   (d) Richard by 4 seconds

Income and Expenditure   15

1 (a) He starts work at 7.00 a.m. but was 15 min late on Wednesday
   (b) 9 h with 1 h for lunch
   (c) 40   (b) 2

2 £140

3 £113.75

4 £195

5

Name: Able Man		Works No. 3475		Date: 21.02.96	
	Nat. Ins. No. ZP 743261 A				
Hours		Payments		Deductions	
Basic	at $1\frac{1}{2}$	Basic pay	£258.40	National Insurance	£7.19
38	$2\frac{1}{2}$	Overtime	£25.50	Income Tax	£42.34
		GROSS PAY	£283.90	Total deductions	£49.53
				NET PAY	£234.37

   (a) (i) £258.40   (ii) £25.50
      (iii) £283.90
   (b) £7.19
   (c) (i) £211.71   (ii) £42.34
   (d) 83%   (e) £10.59

6 £250.80

7 Hollands £227.44, Bennett £201.68, Hogan £200.16, Hyde £213.20

8 £97.45

9 £16 400

10 George, by £174.50

11 (a) £92   (b) 25%
    (c) £300

12 (a) £92   (b) £331.04
    (c) £55.04

13 (a) £6.72   (b) $5\frac{1}{3}$%
14 £95.76
15 (a) 4285   (b) 4845

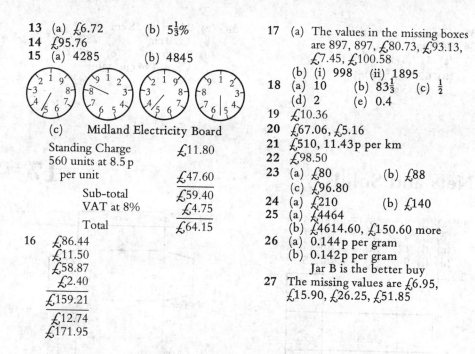

(c)   Midland Electricity Board

Standing Charge	£11.80
560 units at 8.5 p	
per unit	£47.60
Sub-total	£59.40
VAT at 8%	£4.75
Total	£64.15

16   £86.44
     £11.50
     £58.87
     £2.40
     £159.21
     £12.74
     £171.95

17 (a) The values in the missing boxes
       are 897, 897, £80.73, £93.13,
       £7.45, £100.58
     (b) (i) 998   (ii) 1895
18 (a) 10   (b) $83\frac{1}{3}$ (c) $\frac{1}{2}$
     (d) 2   (e) 0.4
19 £10.36
20 £67.06, £5.16
21 £510, 11.43p per km
22 £98.50
23 (a) £80   (b) £88
     (c) £96.80
24 (a) £210   (b) £140
25 (a) £4464
     (b) £4614.60, £150.60 more
26 (a) 0.144 p per gram
     (b) 0.142 p per gram
       Jar B is the better buy
27 The missing values are £6.95,
     £15.90, £26.25, £51.85

Area and Volume

16

1 (a) 48 cm²   (b) 24 cm²
   (c) 48 cm²   (d) 66 cm²
   (e) 78 cm²   (f) 36 cm²
   (g) 84 cm²   (h) 44 cm²
   (i) 20 cm²   (j) 76 cm²
2 (a) 45 cm²   (b) 43 cm²
   (c) 27 cm²   (d) 84 cm²
   (e) 16 cm²   (f) 48 cm²
   (g) 44 cm²   (h) 48 cm²
3 (a) 51 km²   (b) 116 cm²
   (c) 104 m²   (d) 83 m²
   (e) 94 m²   (f) 20 cm²
4 (a) 96 cm²   (b) 160 cm²
   (c) 256 cm²
5 (a) (i) 25 cm²   (ii) 81 cm²
   (b) (i) 32 cm   (ii) $\frac{20}{3}$ cm
6 (a) 12 cm²   (b) 20 cm²
   (c) 30.5 cm²
7 (a) 108 cm   (b) 108 cm
   (c) 384 cm²   (d) 713 cm²
   (e) 329 cm²
8 (a) 6 cm   (b) 36 cm²
   (c) 25 cm²   (d) 11 cm²
   (e) $\sqrt{2}$ cm, 1.414 cm
9 (a) 154, £369.60
   (b) £380
   (c) 47, £117.50
10 8.4 cm by 6.8 cm

11 50 cm², 10 litres
12 450 m³, 4 hours
13 176 cm³
14 (a) 3.5 m²   (b) 5.25 m³
   (c) 6.3 m³   (d) 3.15 tonnes
15 1.62 m³
16 (a) 312 m²   (b) 48 m³
   (c) 30 m³   (d) 92 m²
   (e) 220 m²; 35 cm
17 0.035 m³
18 (a) 66 cm   (b) 150
19 8.8 m, 0.477 m
20 20 m
21 0.2π m, 0.828 m
22 52.5 m
23 44 m
24 482
25 17.09 m²
26 $144\frac{4}{7}$ mm²
27 (a) 154 cm²
   (b) 246 cm²
28 (a) 3850 m²
   (b) 3696 m²
29 (a) 73.4 cm²   (b) 6.95 cm
30 3.281 m²
31 424 cm³
32 8
33 0.0415 m³
34 3.08 cm³, 8

35 45.5%
36 349 cm^3
37 (a) 117.8 cm^3 ($\frac{75}{2}\pi$)
    (b) 62.8 cm^3 (20π)
    (c) 478.5 g

38 (a) 24 cm by 18 cm
    (b) 4320 cm^3 (c) 282.7 cm^3
    (d) 927,6 cm^3 (e) 1272 cm^2
    (f) Yes – 144 cm^2 more
    (g) No

Nets and Solids

17

1 (a) (i) 8   (ii) 5   (iii) 5
   (b) (i) 6   (ii) 4   (iii) 4
   (c) (i) 12   (ii) 8   (iii) 6
   (d) (i) 9   (ii) 6   (iii) 5

2 (a)
   $\frac{1}{3}$ scale

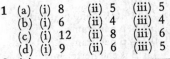

   (b) $\frac{1}{2}$ scale

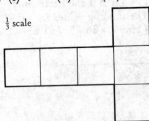

   (c)
   $\frac{1}{2}$ scale

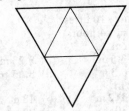

3 (a)

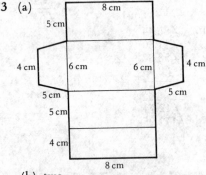

8 cm
5 cm
4 cm   6 cm   6 cm   4 cm
5 cm   5 cm
5 cm
4 cm
8 cm

   (b) two
4 (a) triangles   (b) six
   (c) two, three   (d) six
5 (a) cube
   (b) square pyramid
   (c) cuboid
   (d) triangular prism
   (e) tetrahedron
   (f) open rectangular box
6 (a) cube, square pyramid
   (b) triangular prism, tetrahedron
   (c) cuboid, tetrahedron
   (d) cuboid, cube
   (e) two square pyramids
   (f) two tetrahedrons
7 (a) (i) 8   (ii) 12   (iii) 6
   (b) (i) 6 cm   (ii) 216 cm^3
        (iii) 72 cm
8 (a)
   $\frac{1}{3}$ scale

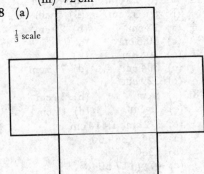

254

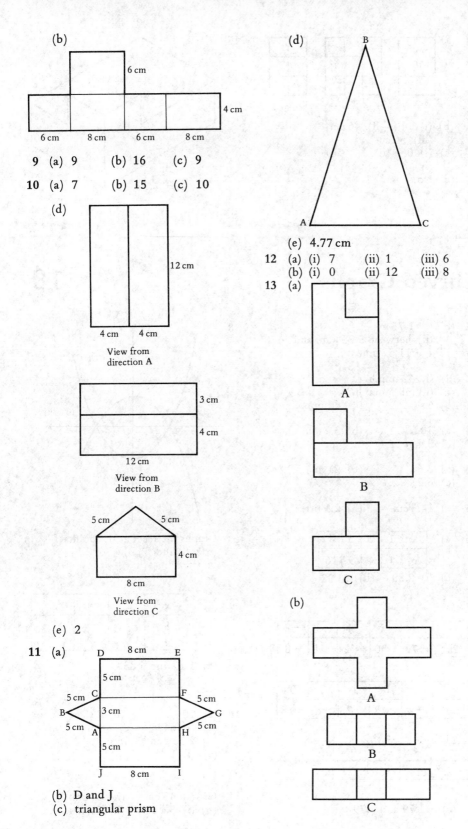

(b)

6 cm

4 cm

6 cm   8 cm   6 cm   8 cm

9 (a) 9   (b) 16   (c) 9

10 (a) 7   (b) 15   (c) 10

(d)

12 cm

4 cm   4 cm

View from
direction A

3 cm

4 cm

12 cm

View from
direction B

5 cm   5 cm

4 cm

8 cm

View from
direction C

(e) 2

11 (a)

D   8 cm   E

5 cm

5 cm C   F 5 cm

B   G

5 cm   3 cm   5 cm

A   H

5 cm

J   8 cm   I

(b) D and J
(c) triangular prism

(d)

B

A   C

(e) 4.77 cm

12 (a) (i) 7   (ii) 1   (iii) 6
     (b) (i) 0   (ii) 12   (iii) 8

13 (a)

A

B

C

(b)

A

B

C

255

14 (a)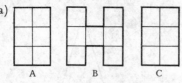

A   B   C

(b) (i) 14   (ii) 46 cm^2
(iii) 56 cm
(c) (i) 0   (ii) 4   (iii) 2
(iv) 8
(d) No

15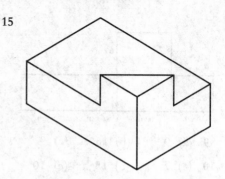

Curved Graphs

18

1 (b) (i) 1.75 m
(ii) between 5.25 a.m. and
11.52 a.m.

2 (a) (i) 42 m.p.h.
(ii) 58.5 m.p.h.
(b) 6 s   (c) 62 m.p.h.

3 (a) 70.5 °C   (b) 3.2 min
(c) 3 min

4 (a) 3.6 s   (b) 21 m
(c) 6.2 s

5 (a) 14.5 cm   (b) 2.1 litres

6 (a)

x	1	2	3	4
x^2	1	4	9	16

(c) (i) 2.89   (ii) ±3.32

7 (a)

x	−6	−5	−4	−3	−2
$-2x^2$	−72	−50	−32	−18	−8

x	1	0	1	2	3
$-2x^2$	−2	0	−2	−8	−18

x	4	5	6
$-2x^2$	−32	−50	−72

(c) −1.79 and 2.79

8

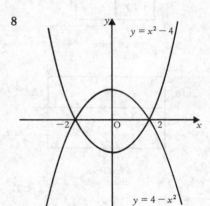

Graphs intersect at the points
(−2, 0) and (2, 0)

9 (a)

x	2	4	6
$\frac{8}{x}$	4	2	1.33

(c) 1.17 and 6.83

10 (a) 10 s   (b) 125 m
(c) (i) 64 m   (ii) 88 m
(d) 2.35 s and 7.65 s
(e) (i) 1.45 s   (ii) 8.55 s

11 (a) (i) 45 cm^2 (ii) 67 cm^2
(b) (i) 5.2 cm   (ii) 7.3 cm

12

x	4	8	10	15
$y°$	90°	45°	36°	24°

(a) (i) 72°   (ii) 28°
(b) 9

13 (a) D   (b) C
   (c) B   (d) A

14 C

15 (a) £112 500
   (b) (i) $\frac{1}{9}$ (ii) $\frac{2}{9}$
   (c) 21st

Trigonometry

1 (a) 6.428   (b) 8.388
   (c) 47.02   (d) 13.44
   (e) 13.74   (f) 8.748
   (g) 2.442   (h) 4.306

2 (a) 10.71   (b) 36.17
   (c) 9.356   (d) 10.54
   (e) 31.13   (f) 18.57

3 (a) 10.71   (b) 56.92
   (c) 8.346   (d) 10.95

4 (a) 8.129   (b) 32.21
   (c) 8.411   (d) 17.20

5 (a) 9.396   (b) 43.82
   (c) 42.31   (d) 39.37

6 (a) 13.86   (b) 27.35
   (c) 5.460   (d) 64.13
   (e) 90.70   (f) 144.9

7 (a) 31.11   (b) 46.60
   (c) 20.24   (d) 79.66
   (e) 229.5   (f) 128.2

8 (a) $\tan C = \dfrac{AD}{DC} = \dfrac{AB}{AC}$

   (b) $\cos B = \dfrac{BD}{AB} = \dfrac{BA}{BC}$

   (c) $\sin B = \dfrac{AD}{AB} = \dfrac{AC}{BC}$

   (d) $\sin C = \dfrac{AD}{AC} = \dfrac{AB}{BC}$

9 (a) $\sin A = \dfrac{BD}{AB}$ (b) $\cos A = \dfrac{AB}{AC}$

   (c) $\tan C = \dfrac{BD}{DC}$ (d) $\sin C = \dfrac{BD}{BC}$

10 (a) $\tan P = \dfrac{SQ}{PS} = \dfrac{RQ}{PQ} = \dfrac{SR}{SQ}$

   (b) $\cos R = \dfrac{SR}{RQ} = \dfrac{RQ}{PR} = \dfrac{SQ}{PQ}$

   (c) $\sin P = \dfrac{SQ}{PQ} = \dfrac{RQ}{PR} = \dfrac{SR}{RQ}$

   (d) $\dfrac{PQ}{RQ} = \dfrac{SQ}{SR} = \dfrac{PS}{SQ}$

11 (a) 20.53°   (b) 65.39°
   (c) 30.62°   (d) 53.65°

12 (a) 35.0°   (b) 39.7°
   (c) 44.4°   (d) 30.3°
   (e) 50.2°   (f) 41.0°

13 (a) 31.3°   (b) 52.4°
   (c) 54.3°   (d) 52.6°

14 (a) 45.6°   (b) 53.1°
   (c) 37.6°   (d) 68.7°
   (e) 11.29 cm   (f) 16.27 cm

15 BD = 36.04 cm, AD = 17.35 cm,
   BC = 83.11 cm

16 BD = 8.386 cm, AD = 11.21 cm,
   $B\hat{C}D = 59.2°$

17 BD = 14.48 cm, AD = 20.38 cm,
   AC = 10.38 cm, $B\hat{C}D = 55.4°$

18 19.53 m

19 35.39 m

20 PQ = 17.73 cm, RQ = 14.04 cm,
   PS = 13.05 cm, PR = 20.35 cm

21 63.39 m

22 (a) 10.67 m   (b) 10.78 m

23 (a) 40.76 m   (b) 96.47 m

24 (a) 11.72 m   (b) 10.34 m

25 (a) 65.27 cm   (b) 41.95 cm
   (c) 91.93 cm   (d) 77.79 cm

26 (a) 90°   (b) 31.6°
   (c) 7.63 km   (d) 222°

27 (a) 4.142 m   (b) 10.82 m

28 (a) 2.106 km   (b) 2.795 km
   (c) 37°

29 (a) $p = 60°$, $q = 30°$, $r = 120°$,
     $s = 60°$
   (b) (i) 5.196 m   (ii) 1.50 m

Quadratic Equations   **20**

1 $(x+3)(x+4)$	**2** $(x+2)(x+7)$	**23** $5, -9$	**24** $-5, -7$
3 $(a+4)(a+7)$	**4** $(m+6)(m+7)$	**25** $-3, 7$	**26** $1, 3$
5 $(x+4)(x-3)$	**6** $(x+7)(x-2)$	**27** $3, 9$	**28** $-2, -3$
7 $(b+4)(b-7)$	**8** $(x-9)(x+2)$	**29** $3, 10$	**30** $-10, 4$
9 $(a-4)(a-5)$	**10** $(x-2)(x-7)$		
11 $(x-7)(x-8)$	**12** $(x-3)(x-5)$	**31** $7, 12$	**32** $9, 13$
		33 $4, 5, 6$	**34** $7, 13$
13 $2, 8$	**14** $5, 2$	**35** 8 cm	**36** $7 \text{ cm}, 14 \text{ cm}$
15 $-8, 9$	**16** $4, 7$	**37** $5 \text{ cm}, 12 \text{ cm}$	**38** $20 \text{ m by } 18 \text{ m}$
17 $-4, 5$	**18** $3, -6$	**39** $8, 10, 12$	**40** 277 cm^2
19 $-4, -7$	**20** $-3, -8$	**41** 3	
21 $4, 7$	**22** $5, 6$		

Inequalities and Regions   **21**

1 (a) $x < 1$

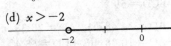

(b) $x > 1$

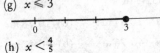

(c) $x < 2$

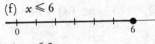

(d) $x > -2$

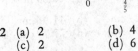

(e) $x > -1.5$

(f) $x \leqslant 6$

(g) $x \leqslant 3$

(h) $x < \frac{4}{5}$

2 (a) 2   (b) 4
    (c) 2   (d) 6

3 (a) $3, 4, 5, 6, 7, 8$
    (b) $5, 6, 7, 8, 9$

4 (a) $1 < x \leqslant 3$ (b) $-2 < x < 2$
    (c) $-3 \leqslant x < 2$ (d) $-5 \leqslant x \leqslant 2$

5 (a) $x \leqslant -2$ and $x \geqslant 2$
    (b) $-3 \leqslant x \leqslant 3$
    (c) $x < -2.5$ and $x > 2.5$
    (d) $-\frac{4}{3} < x < \frac{4}{3}$

6

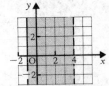

$(-1, 3)$ and $(2, 2)$ lie within the region, $(4, 2)$ does not

In questions 7 to 10 solid lines are assumed to belong to the shaded regions whereas dashed lines do not.

7 $x \leqslant 3$, yes   **8** $y < 2$, no
9 $x < -2$, no   **10** $-2 < y < 1$, no

11

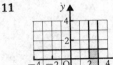

12

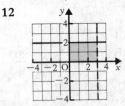

13

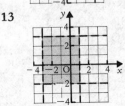

14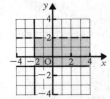

15 $-2 \leqslant x \leqslant 1, \ y \geqslant -2$
16 $-1 < x \leqslant 1, \ -1 \leqslant y \leqslant 4$
17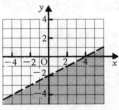

18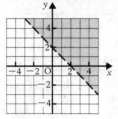

19 $x + y > 4$
20 $3y - 2x < 6$
21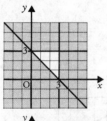

22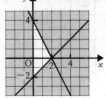

23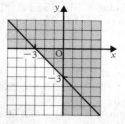

24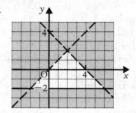

25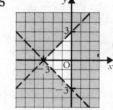

26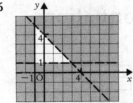

27 (a) $x = 2y, \ x + y < 25$
     (b) 1,2,3,4,5,6,7,8 years old
        $1 \leqslant y \leqslant 8$

Time and Travel   22

1 (a) 16 May   (b) 7 May
2 (a) 24 April   (b) 3 May
3 25 August
4 20 July
5 13
6 11

7 47
8 12
9 (a) 13   (b) 68   (c) 12
10 (a) 8.25 a.m.   (b) 10.20 a.m.
     (c) 1 h 15 min   (d) 3 h
     (e) 2 h 35 min   (f) 7 h 30 min

11 (a) 1 h 35 min   (b) 55 min
    (c) 40 min   (d) 3 h
    (e) 20 min   (f) 6 min
    (g) 2 h 30 min
12 12 h 39 min
13 14 h 58 min
14 (a) 6 min 6 s   (b) 10 min 20 s
    (c) 8 min 8 s
    (d) (i) 5 min 54 s   (ii) 9 min 50 s
    (e) (i) 20 min 20 s (ii) 19 min 40 s
    (f) 1 min 56 s
    (g) (i) 2.067 min   (ii) 0.034 h
    (h) 3.7 miles
15 (a) 215 miles   (b) 199 miles
16 Cambridge by 18 miles
17 (a) Cambridge   (b) Edinburgh
18 (a) London   (b) York
19 (a) York and Leeds
    (b) London and Edinburgh
20 (a) 2.30 p.m.   (b) 1430
21 (a) 130 p   (b) 225 p
    (c) 350 p   (d) 940 p
22 (a) 9 minutes   (b) one
    (c) 12.05   (d) 10.52
    (e) one   (f) 11.05
    (g) 150 km/h

23 (a) 3 p.m.   (b) 8 a.m.
24 8.30 a.m.
25 (a) During the week commencing
         25 July
    (b) More people wish to travel at the
         weekend
    (c) Hotel Bali
26 £1344.25, £160
27 (a) £165
    (b) £1304.25, £47.25
28 (a) Sesin
    (b) (i) £517   (ii) £295   (iii) £275
    (c) Yes
    (d) £1145.40; no, including £250
         spending money they are £45.40
         over.
29 (a) $510   (b) 943 f.
    (c) 8277 pta   (d) 620 DM
30 £1 = $1.72
31 £1 = 170 pta
32 £36
33 No, £16 cheaper at home
34 £11 500
35 (a) 360 pta   (b) £2.25
36 4 (nearly)

Transformations   23

1 (a)

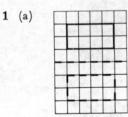

   (b)

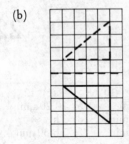

   (c)

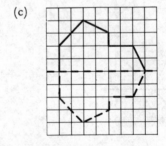

   (d)

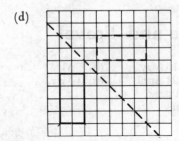

260

(e)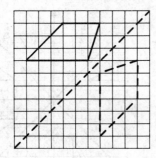

2 (a)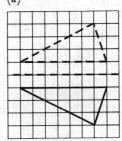

(b)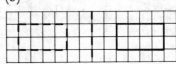

(f)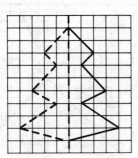

(c)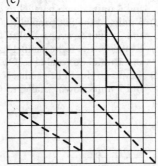

(g)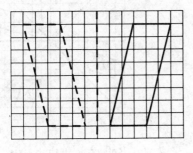

(d)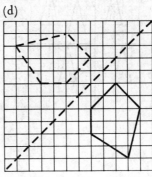

(h)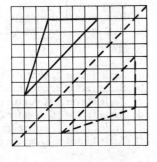

3 (a) (b)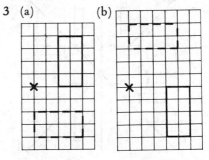

(c)

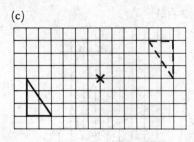

(d)

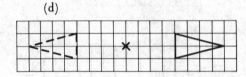

4 (a) 4 units to the right parallel to Ox
        and 4 units down parallel to Oy
   (b) 5 units to the left parallel to Ox
        and 7 units down parallel to Oy
   (c) 6 units to the right parallel to Ox
        and 5 units up parallel to Oy
   (d) 8 units to the right parallel to Ox
        and 7 units down parallel to Oy

5

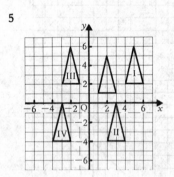

6 (a)

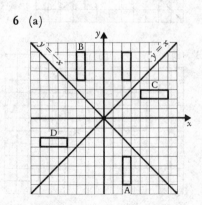

(b)

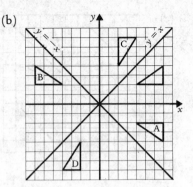

(c)

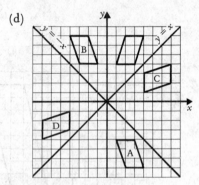

(d)

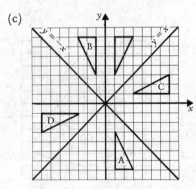

7 (a) Reflection in the x-axis
   (b) Translation of 8 units to the left
        parallel to Ox and 9 units down
        parallel to Oy
   (c) Rotation about the origin
        through $180°$
   (d) Reflection in the y-axis
   (e) Reflection in the line whose
        equation is $y = x$

8 (a) Scale factor 2, centre $(0, 0)$
   (b) Scale factor 2, centre $(-1, 2)$
   (c) Scale factor $-\frac{1}{2}$, centre $(0, 0)$
   (d) Scale factor -1, centre $(2, -2)$
   (e) Scale factor $\frac{1}{2}$, centre $(-5, -8)$
   (f) Scale factor -2, centre $(2, 1)$

262

9 (a)

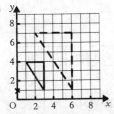

(b)

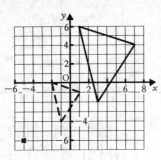

10

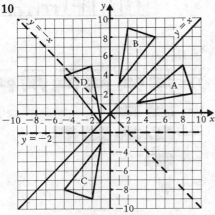

(c) A reflection in the line with equation $y = -x$

(e) $(2, -2)$, $90°$ anticlockwise

11

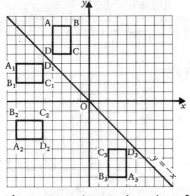

(d) Rotation about O through $180°$

12 (a) Reflection in the line with equation $y = -3$

(b) Reflection in the line with equation $x = -2$

(c) Enlargement, centre $(0, -2)$, scale factor 2

(d) B, C and E

(e) B, C, E, G, H

(f) 12 units to the right parallel to Ox and 6 units down parallel to Oy

13

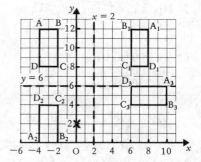

14 (a) $A(-6, 1)$, $B(-1, 3)$, $C(-5, 5)$

(b) 10 units to the right parallel to Ox and 3 units up parallel to Oy

(c)

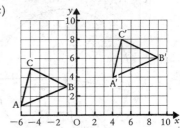

(d) $A'(4, 4)$, $B'(9, 6)$, $C'(5, 8)$

15 (a) $(4, 2)$ (b) $(5, 1)$

263

Statistics

24

1 (a) (i) BL (ii) Korean
   (b) (i) 7 (ii) 10
   (c) 29   (d) 8

2 (a) a dog   (b) 6
   (c) 58
   (d) Dogs, cats, birds, rabbits, fish, gerbils

3 (a) Tuesday
   (b) 830
   (c) a holiday
   (d) 80

4 (a) 1950   (b) 390
   (c) 4680

5 (a) $\frac{8}{15}$ (b) £225
   (c) £125   (d) £625
   (e) 20%

6 (a) 900 hectares
   (b) 100°
   (c) 270 hectares

7 (a) 15%
   (b) (i) 198°   (ii) 36°
   (d) 11:2
   (e) (i) £5 544 000 (ii) £1 512 000

8 (a) 30
   (b)

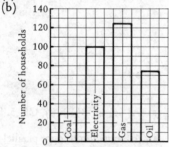

   (c) 3:5   (d) $\frac{1}{12}$
   (e)

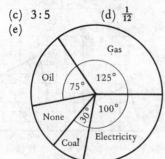

9 (a) 23   (b) 59

10 (a) 560 (b) 190 (c) 1:4

11 (a)

Vehicle	Total
Car	18
Bus	6
Lorry	12
Van	3
Other	1
	40

   (b) 40   (c) car   (d) 3:2
   (e) Fire engine — or any other suitable alternative
   (f) (i) 2025   (ii) 675
   (g)

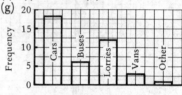

   (h)

12 (a) True   (b) True
   (c) False   (d) True
   (e) Not known (f) False

13 (a) (i) 700 (ii) 550
   (b) No
   (c) Its production per employee may be much higher than all the others

14

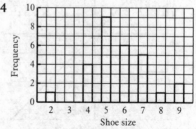

   (a) 28   (b) 5   (c) 14

15

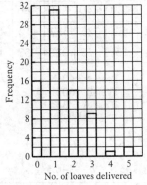

No. of loaves delivered

(a) 73　　(b) 57　　(c) 100

16

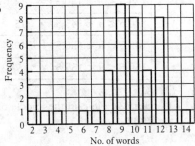

No. of words

(a) 42　　(b) 11　　(c) 397
(d) 9　　(e) 12

17

	Mean	Median	Mode
(a)	18	16	16
(b)	30	29	29
(c)	75	73	70, 71

18　(a) 49　　(b) 1　　(c) 2
　　(d) 85　　(e) 1.73　　(f) 6

19　(a) 169 cm　　(b) 169 cm
　　(c) 169 cm

20　mean 75, median 71, mode 70

21　mean 1.5, median 1, mode 0

22　(a) 160 cm　　(b) 160 cm
　　(c) 160 cm

23　(a) £1.76　　(b) £1.80

24　(a) £3.17　　(b) £3.10
　　(c) £3.10

25　(a) (i) 10　(ii) 13　(iii) 4
　　(b) 48　(c) 1　(d) 93
　　(e) 1.94　(f) 2

26　(a), (d)

27　(a) (i) 3rd diagram
　　　　(ii) 2nd diagram
　　(b) 5000　　(c) 82 500
　　(d) 14.5%

28　(a) 214
　　(b)

Marks	<10	<20	<30	<40	<50
Cumulative frequency	9	46	104	177	214

(c) 37
(d)

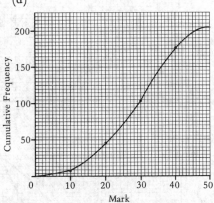

Median mark 30 (to nearest whole number)

29　(a) and (c)

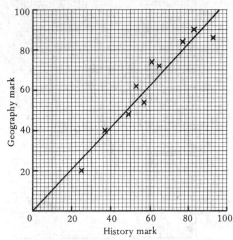

(b) History 60, Geography 63
(d) 51

30 (a)

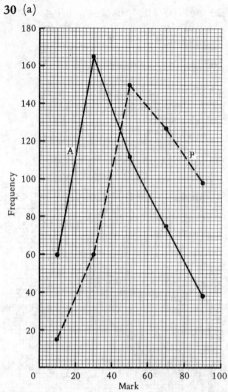

Mark	≤20	≤40	≤60	≤80	≤100
Test A	60	225	337	412	450
Test B	15	75	225	352	450

(c) (i) Test A 40
　　　 Test B 60
　　(ii) Test A 34
　　　　 Test B 33

31 (a) 133 cm
　　(b) $145.5 \leqslant h < 146.5$

(c)

Height, h cm	Frequency
$130.5 \leqslant h < 135.5$	5
$135.5 \leqslant h < 140.5$	14
$140.5 \leqslant h < 145.5$	15
$145.5 \leqslant h < 150.5$	19
$150.5 \leqslant h < 155.5$	7

(d) 34
(e) Because 148 is in the middle of a group

(b)

266

Probability

25

1 (a) $\frac{1}{4}$ (b) $\frac{3}{4}$ (c) $\frac{1}{13}$
    (d) $\frac{1}{26}$ (e) $\frac{1}{52}$ (f) $\frac{3}{26}$

2 (a) $\frac{5}{26}$ (b) $\frac{21}{26}$ (c) $\frac{3}{13}$

3 (a) $\frac{1}{5}$ (b) $\frac{2}{5}$ (c) $\frac{1}{25}$
    (d) $\frac{22}{25}$

4

		'A' team		
		B	G	G
'B' team	G	(G, B)	(G, G)	(G, G)
	B	(B, B)	(B, G)	(B, G)
	B	(B, B)	(B, G)	(B, G)

(a) (i) $\frac{2}{9}$ (ii) $\frac{5}{9}$

(b)

		'A' team	
		G	G
'B' team	G	(G, G)	(G, G)
	B	(B, G)	(B, G)

(c) (i) $\frac{1}{2}$ (ii) 0

5

	1	2	3	4	5	6
1	2	3	4	5	6	7
2	3	4	5	6	7	8
3	4	5	6	7	8	9
4	5	6	7	8	9	10
5	6	7	8	9	10	11
6	7	8	9	10	11	12

(a) 12, once, $\frac{1}{36}$

(b) 2, once, $\frac{1}{36}$

(c) five, $\frac{5}{36}$

(d) 7

(e) (i) $\frac{1}{2}$ (ii) $\frac{5}{12}$

6

	1	3	5	7	9	11
2	3	5	7	9	11	13
4	5	7	9	11	13	15
6	7	9	11	13	15	17
8	9	11	13	15	17	19
10	11	13	15	17	19	21
12	13	15	17	19	21	23

(a) 23, $\frac{1}{36}$ (b) 3

(c) 0   (d) 1

(e) (i) $\frac{1}{12}$ (ii) $\frac{5}{36}$ (iii) $\frac{1}{6}$

7 (a) $\frac{1}{20}$ (b) $\frac{19}{20}$

8 $\frac{4}{9}$

9 (a) $\frac{3}{5}$ (b) 1

10 (a) $\frac{1}{6}$ (b) $\frac{2}{3}$ (c) $\frac{5}{6}$

11 (a) $\frac{1}{6}$ (b) $\frac{1}{36}$ (c) $\frac{1}{4}$

12 (a) $\frac{1}{36}$ (b) $\frac{1}{9}$ (c) 1
    (d) 0

13 (a) (i) $\frac{4}{15}$ (ii) $\frac{2}{5}$
    (b) (i) $\frac{1}{35}$ (ii) $\frac{3}{7}$

14

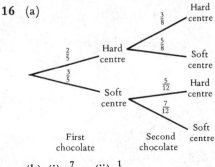

First coin   Second coin

$P(50p) = \frac{2}{3}$, $P(£1) = \frac{1}{3}$, $P(50p) = \frac{5}{8}$, $P(£1) = \frac{3}{8}$, $P(50p) = \frac{3}{4}$, $P(£1) = \frac{1}{4}$

(a) $\frac{5}{12}$ (b) $\frac{1}{12}$ (c) $\frac{1}{4}$
(d) $\frac{1}{2}$

15 (a) $\frac{2}{5}$

First girl   Second girl

$P(E) = \frac{3}{5}$, $P(NE) = \frac{2}{5}$, $P(E) = \frac{3}{5}$, $P(NE) = \frac{2}{5}$, $P(E) = \frac{3}{5}$, $P(NE) = \frac{2}{5}$

(b) (i) $\frac{4}{25}$ (ii) $\frac{6}{25}$ (iii) $\frac{12}{25}$

16 (a)

First chocolate   Second chocolate

$\frac{2}{5}$ Hard centre, $\frac{3}{5}$ Soft centre, $\frac{3}{8}$ Hard centre, $\frac{5}{8}$ Soft centre, $\frac{5}{12}$ Hard centre, $\frac{7}{12}$ Soft centre

(b) (i) $\frac{7}{20}$ (ii) $\frac{1}{2}$

17 (a) (i) $\frac{5}{8}$ (ii) $\frac{1}{4}$ (iii) $\frac{1}{4}$

(b) 20 (c) 25

(d)

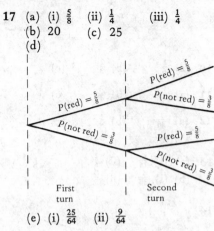

First turn | Second turn

$P(\text{red}) = \frac{5}{8}$

$P(\text{not red}) = \frac{3}{8}$

$P(\text{red}) = \frac{5}{8}$

$P(\text{not red}) = \frac{3}{8}$

$P(\text{red}) = \frac{5}{8}$

$P(\text{not red}) = \frac{3}{8}$

(e) (i) $\frac{25}{64}$ (ii) $\frac{9}{64}$

18 (a)

Time (t seconds)	Frequency
$10 < t \leqslant 11$	2
$11 < t \leqslant 12$	9
$12 < t \leqslant 13$	25
$13 < t \leqslant 14$	27
$14 < t \leqslant 15$	37

(b) 100 (c) 0.89

(d) 0.52

19 (a) (i) $\frac{9}{16}$ (ii) $\frac{1}{16}$

(b)

Bulb from bag

$P(\text{'red' bulb}) = \frac{3}{4}$

$P(\text{'white' bulb}) = \frac{1}{4}$

$P(\text{flowers}) = \frac{7}{8}$

$P(\text{does not flower}) = \frac{1}{8}$

$P(\text{flowers}) = \frac{9}{10}$

$P(\text{does not flower}) = \frac{1}{10}$

(c) (i) $\frac{9}{40}$ (ii) $\frac{19}{160}$

(d) (i) 210 (ii) 38

(e) Yes, since 34 bulbs would be expected to fail

Solving Equations by Trial and Improvement

26

1 5.4 and 5.5
2 5.0 and 5.1
3 6.6 and 6.7
4 4.6 and 4.7
5 6.8 and 6.9

6 5.7 and 5.8
7 4.1 and 4.2
8 4.6 and 4.7
9 8.1 and 8.2
10 3.3 and 3.4

Part 2:   Revision Papers 1–24

Revision Paper

1

1 (a) 50p, 50p, 10p, 5p
   (b) 0.444, 0.45, 0.54
2 (a) $12x$ (b) $4x$
   (c) $32x^2$ (d) -4
3 (a) 7
   (b) (i) $x = \frac{2}{3}$ (ii) $x = 9$
       (iii) $x = 3$ or $x = 8$
4 1600
5 (a) (i) $\sin A$ (ii) $\cos A$
       (iii) $\tan A$
   (b) (i) $30°$ (ii) 34.6 cm
6 $310°$
7 $y = 3x - 5$
8 $x = 4$, $y = 5$

9 $a = 132°$, $b = 90°$, $c = 48°$,
   $d = 48°$, $e = 42°$
10 (a) (i) $45°$ (ii) $135°$
    (b) No, $135°$ will not divide exactly
        into $360°$
11 £9
12 (a) 21
    (b) 39
    (c) 11

No. of goals scored

Revision Paper

2

1 (a)   (i) $5\frac{23}{40}$ (ii) $3\frac{3}{10}$
       (iii) 15   (iv) 6
   (b)   (i) $13a$ (ii) $15ab$
       (iii) -50 (iv) -8
2 (a) $x - 21$ (b) x^2
   (c) $x^2 - 6x - 40$
   (d) $x^2 - 25$
3 (a) (i) 250 i.e. 2.5×10^2
       (ii) 247   (iii) 246.7
   (b) 499.5
   (c) (i) 416 km   (ii) 350 miles
4 (a) (i) $x = 3$ (ii) $x = 5$
       (iii) $x = 5$ or -5
   (b) (i) 1, 2, 3, 4   (ii) 5   (iii) 7
5 $a = 60°$, $b = 67°$, $c = 46°$,
   $d = 74°$
6 (a) AB = 116 mm, AC = 96 mm,
       BC = 46 mm;
       perimeter = 258 mm
   (b) Obtuse angle; $\hat{A} = 22°$,
       $\hat{B} = 54°$, $\hat{C} = 104°$; sum = $180°$
7 (a) Reflection in the line $y = x$
   (b) Translation parallel to the
       x-axis
   (c) Reflection in the x-axis
   (d) Reflection in the y-axis
   (e) Rotation about the origin
       through $180°$
   (f) Reflection in the line $y = -x$

8 (a) £177.60   (b) £198
9 (a) $60°, 150°, 15°, 75°$
   (b) (i) 5.20 m   (ii) 11.20 m
   (c) 51.6 m^2
10 (a)

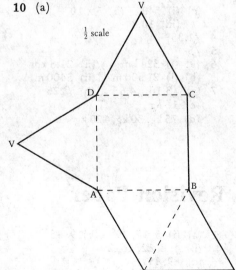

$\frac{1}{2}$ scale

   (b) 8.66 cm
11 (a) $\frac{1}{4}$ (b) $\frac{3}{4}$ (c) $\frac{1}{13}$
    (d) $\frac{1}{26}$ (e) $\frac{1}{52}$ (f) $\frac{1}{26}$
12 (a) (i) $(0, 12)$ (ii) $y = -2x + 12$
    (b) (i) $(-6, 0)$ (ii) 2
        (iii) $y = 2x + 12$

Revision Paper 3

1. (a) 7
   (b) (i) 9.928×10^{-1}
       (ii) 2.83×10^5
2. 12.38
3. (a) 14.3 cm   (b) 4.64 cm
   (c) 43.9 cm
4. $p = 47°$, $q = 43°$, $r = 90°$,
   $s = 33°$, $t = 57°$, $u = 76°$
5. 10.30, 42 m.p.h.
6. (a) (i) 4 h 5 min   (ii) 9 h 20 min
   (b) 10 lb   (c) $T = 35(P + 1)$
7. (a) -23 (b) 9
   (c) 12   (d) 1
8. (a) $x = 5\frac{1}{2}$ (b) $x = 6$
   (c) $x = 11$ (d) $x = 7$
   (e) $x = 2$ or 9   (f) $x = -4$ or 7
9. (a) (i) 030°   (ii) 070°
       (iii) 250°
   (b) 14.7 km, 083°
10. 5 cm
11. (a) £38 430   (b) £12 810
12. (a) (i) New York
        (ii) Anchorage
    (b) 42°C
    (c) (i) Singapore (3°C)
        (ii) New York (42°C)

Revision Paper 4

1. (a) $x = 5$ (b) $x = 13$
   (c) $x = 6$ (d) $x = 1\frac{1}{2}$
   (e) $x = -7$ or -9 (f) $x = -3$ or $1\frac{1}{2}$
2. (a) $x = 33°$, $y = 71°$
   (b) $z = 105°$
3. (a) $3.5 \leqslant l < 4.5$
   (b) (i) 10^6 (ii) 2.5×10^3 or 2500
   (c) (i) 540   (ii) 5×10^4
       (iii) 10.8
4. £1.35
5. £5
6. (a) (i) 324 km   (ii) 21.6 km
   (b) (i) 21 600 m   (ii) 5400 m
7. (a) £3.10, £4.65   (b) £225
   (c) 16 kg
   (d) 75 kg, 30 kg, 120 kg
8. (a) £120   (b) 25
   (c) £3200   (d) £128
9. (a) $\pi r(r + 2h)$
   (b) $3b(a - 4c)$
   (c) $4x(2x - 3)$
   (d) $2\pi r^2(r + 2h)$
   (e) $(x + 4)(x - 4)$
   (f) $(x + 7)(x - 3)$
10. $\frac{3}{16}''$
11. 11.9 miles, 226.5°
12. (a) $(x + 20)$ cm, $(x + 40)$ cm
    (b) 1.5 m, 1.7 m, 1.9 m

Revision Paper 5

1. (a) (i) 5, 17, 29   (ii) 9, 45
   (b) 4, 8, 12, 16, 20
   (c) 89, 117
2. (a) $3x(x + 2y)$ (b) $x(x - 6)$
   (c) $3(2x^2 + 1)$ (d) $x(6 + x)$
   (e) $(x - 3)(x - 5)$ (f) $(x + 4)(x - 5)$
3. (a) 1.2×10^3 (b) 4.8×10^5
4. 20p, 20p, 10p, 5p, 2p, 1p
5. 50 m correct to the nearest metre
6. £173
7. (a) $\dfrac{v^2 - u^2}{2a}$ (b) (i) 2   (ii) 6
8. (a) (i) 45   (ii) 10   (iii) 21
   (b) 40%
9. $R^2 = \dfrac{A}{\pi} + r^2$, $R = \sqrt{\dfrac{A}{\pi} + r^2}$
10. (a) 8.94 km   (b) 288.4°
11. 44 square units
12. 2.69 and -1.49

Revision Paper 6

1 (a) £6.40
   (b) $3\frac{1}{2}$ hours, 40 m.p.h.
2 (a) 37, 50
   (b) 27, ..., $\frac{1}{3}$, $\frac{1}{9}$
   (c) 144, ..., 576
3 (a) (i) $9(x-2)$ (ii) $3x(3x+1)$
        (iii) $\pi r(2r+h)$
   (b) (i) $6x+23$
        (ii) $x^2-5x-36$
4 (a) 18 cm by 15 cm
   (b) 270 cm^2
5 AP = 6.7 cm
6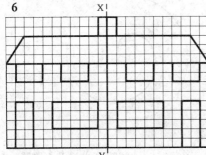

7 (a) $37\frac{1}{2}\%$
   (b) £360
   (c) £630
8 (a) A reflection in the y-axis
   (b) A reflection in the x-axis
   (c) An enlargement, centre (0, 0),
       scale factor 2
   (d) A rotation, about the origin,
       through 180°
   (e) A rotation, about the origin,
       through 180°
   (f) A reflection in the y-axis
9 (a) 47 h
   (b) £241.88 (to nearest penny)
10 $x = 6.25$ cm, $y = 5.83$ cm,
    $z = 8.55$ cm
11 (a) 70 m
   (b) 19.3°
12 (a) 48 m.p.h.
   (b) 4
   (c) 11.45
   (d) 269 km

Revision Paper 7

1 (a) $6\frac{1}{4}$ (b) $2\frac{1}{2}$
   (c) $1\frac{3}{4}$ (d) 5
2 (a) $2x+6y$ (b) $12a^2$
   (c) $9a^6$ (d) $2ab$
3 (a) 1 to 200
   (b) (i) 750 m (ii) 4.3 cm^2 (iii) 0.5 m^3
4 13, £2.32
5 (a) 6p   (b) £60
6 $x = 37°$, $y = 26°$, $z = 27°$
7 87.3 m
8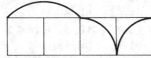

9 (a) AC = 10 cm
   (b) 3 cm, 4 cm, 5 cm
   (c) $\frac{9}{2}\pi$ cm^2, 8π cm^2, $\frac{25}{2}\pi$ cm^2
   (d) area of Z = area of X + area of Y
   (e) No
10 (a) 11   (b) 92
11 (a) £1925   (b) £1170
   (c) £3095   (d) 24 375 km
   (e) 12.7 p, 38%
12 (a) 37   (b) 6   (c) 11
   (d) 19   (e) 10   (f) 62

Revision Paper 8

1 £12 800
2 (a) 2   (b) 25
   (c) −24
3 (a) 100°   (b) 108°
   (c) 200°

4 (a) (i) $D = \dfrac{C}{\pi}$
        (ii) $D = \sqrt{\dfrac{4A}{\pi}}$, $A = \dfrac{C}{4\pi}$
   (b) (i) 22.7 ℓ (ii) 11 gal (approx)

5 (a) 63°   (b) 41°
   (c) (i) 57.5 m   (ii) 25.5 m
6 (a) £175   (b) £8400
   (c) £12 350
   (d) The building worker
   (e) The trainee architect
7 (a) 30.8 m   (b) 57.7°
8 (a) −7, 5   (b) 4, −7
   (c) 1.5, −1.5   (d) −5, 5

9 (a) 4   (b) 16   (c) 148
10 (a) (i) $\frac{1}{6}$ (ii) $\frac{2}{3}$
   (b) (i) $\frac{1}{36}$ (ii) $\frac{1}{3}$ (iii) $\frac{7}{18}$
     (iv) $\frac{11}{36}$
11 (a) 2.82 m   (b) 2.32 m
   (c) 4.10 m^2 (d) 40°
   (e) 0.64 m
12 about £36 000

Revision Paper 9

1 (a) 5   (b) 0.0027

2 (a) T   (b) F
   (c) T   (d) F
   (e) F   (f) T

3 (a) 4   (b) 25
   (c) 7

4 $a = 9$ cm, $b = 15$ cm

5 54.7 p/l

6 £7

7 £4775.68

8 3.875 m

9 238.8 cm^2

10 (a) 8 h
   (b) $3\frac{1}{2}$ h
   (c) £273.49

11

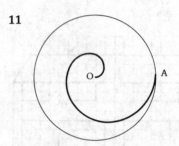

12

	Length (m)	Width (m)	Area (m²)
Lounge	6	5	30
Dining room	5	4	20
Kitchen	5	4	20
Hall	4	4	16
Bathroom	3	2	6
Bedroom 1	5	4	20
Bedroom 2	5	4	20

Revision Paper 10

1 (a) 4   (b) 8
   (c) 10   (d) 5

2 9 °C

3 (a) a regular pentagon
   (b) 108°
   (c) 72°
   (d) No, 108° will not divide exactly
      into 360°

4 £71.02, £62.48

5 35 m

6 (a) 35 cm   (b) 14 cm
   (c) 140 m^3

7 (a) A(0, 5), B(4, 0)
   (b) $-\frac{5}{4}$
   (c) (i) $-\frac{5}{4}$ (ii) 5
   (d) $x \geqslant 0,\ y \geqslant 0,\ 5x + 4y \leqslant 20$
8 (a) (i) 7 p   (ii) 49 p
   (b) 200 g jar (cheapest cost per
      gram)
9

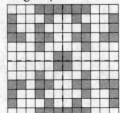

10 (a) 1 : 20 000
   (b) (i) 6 cm
      (ii) 18.75 km

11 (a) (i) 1.08×10^9 km
      (ii) 2.592×10^{10} km
   (b) 4.4 years

12 (a) (i)   (ii)

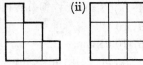

   (b) 18
   (c) (i) 36
      (ii) 120 cm by 90 cm by 90 cm
   (d) (i) 4   (ii) 6   (iii) 6

Revision Paper   11

1 (a) (i) 0.5625   (ii) 56.25%
   (b) (i) 355%   (ii) 3.5%
   (c) 0.074, 0.47, 0.471, 0.741

2 (a) $\frac{2}{3}$ (b) $\frac{200}{3}$ (c) $\frac{5}{11}$
   (d) $\frac{500}{11}$

3

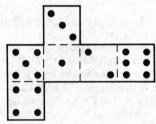

4 122 m

5 (a) (i) 100   (ii) 1200
   (b) (i) 10 min   (ii) 250 min

6 (a) 165°   (b) 4 to 3
   (c) (i) 36   (ii) 132

7 (a)

Date	Meter reading	Number of units used in quarter
6 Nov	14 563	
10 Feb	15 543	First 980
4 May	16 567	Second 1024
12 Aug	16 993	Third 426
8 Nov	17 635	Fourth 642

   (b) £97.90, £101.70, £50.04, £68.70

8 (a)

Number of goals scored per match	Tally	Frequency
0	ꓱꓱꓱꓱ IIII	9
1	ꓱꓱꓱꓱ ꓱꓱꓱꓱ I	11
2	ꓱꓱꓱꓱ IIII	9
3	ꓱꓱꓱꓱ II	7
4	IIII	4
5	III	3
6	II	2

   (b) 45
   (c)

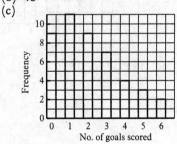

   (d) 2.07, 1, 2
   (e) $\frac{1}{5}$

9 41 sq units

10 (a) (i) No   (ii) Yes
   (b) (i) 9 cm   (ii) 5 cm
   (c) 4 : 1

Revision Paper   12

1 14

2 (a) 52.4 m   (b) 493 g
   (c) 0.5 m^2 (d) 1 cm^3

3 (a) 10   (b) 12   (c) -8
   (d) $17a$ (e) $15a^2$ (f) 3
   (g) $12a^5$ (h) $\frac{1}{a}$ (i) -4

4 (a) 7 a.m.   (b) 11 p.m.
5 10
6 10.05 a.m.
7 (a) 6   (b) 6   (c) 5, 6   (d) 8
8 (a) (i) E   (ii) A
   (b) $\frac{1}{400}$ (c) $\frac{3}{10}$

9 (a) A: 4 cm × 2 cm × 3 cm,
       B: 6 cm × 4 cm × 2 cm,
       C: 8 cm × 6 cm × 1 cm
   (b) A: 44 cm^2, B: 64 cm^2,
       C: 76 cm^2
   (c) A: 24 cm^3, B: 48 cm^3,
       C: 48 cm^3
10 0.968 m

Revision Paper   13

1 20 °C
2 393
3 24.8 cm
4 (a) 216 m^2 (b) 10.8 kg
   (c) 11
5 (a) (i) 45°   (ii) 67.5°
       (iii) 67.5°
   (b) 2.12 cm, 7.24 cm, 3.62 cm
   (c) 3.62 cm
   (d) (i) 5.43 cm^2 (ii) 5.43 cm^2
6 (a) 188
   (b)

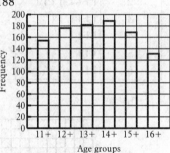

   (c) 13+   (d) 14+   (e) $\frac{3}{10}$

7
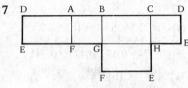

(The letters indicate the original
position on the cuboid.)

8 (a) An enlargement, centre (0, 0),
       scale factor 2
   (b) Rotation anticlockwise about
       the origin through 90°
   (c) Reflection in the line $y = -x$
   (d) A translation of 2 units to the left
       parallel to Ox and 6 units up
       parallel to Oy
   (e) Reflection in the x-axis
9 (a) 540
   (b) (i) 2 h 15 min   (ii) 54 min
   (c) 60
10 (a) 267 785   (b) 176 195
    (c) 26 779
    (d)

No. of goals	Frequency
0	2
1	8
2	6
3	3
4	1

    (e) mean 1.65, mode 1, median 1.5

Revision Paper   14

1 (a) 54 000   (b) 54 500
   (c) 54 500   (d) 50 000

2 If l cm is the actual length, b cm
   the actual width and A cm^2 the
   actual area then
   (a) $l < 120.5$ (b) $b \geqslant 81.5$

   (c) $A < 9941.25$
   (d) $9739.25 \geqslant A$
3 $56\frac{1}{2}$ kg
4 (a) 35   (b) 85
5 (a) 6 p.m.
   (b) 4 p.m. same day
6 (a) £2623.04   (b) £383.04

7 (a) $\frac{3}{7}$
   (b)

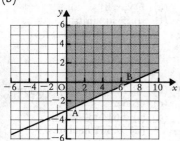

8 (a) 8.67   (b) 7.68, 1.6
9 (a) $x(2.7-x)\,\mathrm{m}^2$
   (c) $y = 1.6$ when $x = 0$
       $y = -0.1$ when $x = 1$
   (d) 0.88 m
10 (a) (i) 190 f.   (ii) £18.50
       (iii) 9.50 f.
   (c) the French tourist in Britain

Revision Paper   15

1 (a) 2
   (b) 1.6
2 (a) £7.20
   (b) £1.80
   (c) £1.80
3 (a) £613.98
   (b) £2.80
4 (a) 0.321, 0.32, 0.23, 0.032
   (b) (i)
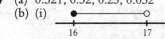
   If the age is denoted by y years
   $16 \leqslant y < 17$
   (ii)
   If the length is l m
   $29 < l \leqslant 30$
   (iii)
   If the mass is m kg
   $19.5 \leqslant m < 20.5$
5 (a) 4 cm
   (b) 12.4 cm
6 5.87

7 (a) (i) $3\frac{1}{3}$ h   (ii) $6\frac{2}{3}$ h
   (b) $M = 50(W + 1)$
   (c) $M = \frac{5}{6}(W + 1)$
8 (a) £68   (b) £150
9 (a)

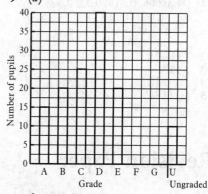

   (b) (i) 40   (ii) 60
   (c) (i) $\frac{4}{13}$ (ii) $\frac{7}{26}$
10 (a) a parallelogram
   (b) (i) 480 cm^2 (ii) 1440 cm^2
       (iii) 480 cm^2
   (c) $\frac{1}{3}$

Revision Paper   16

1 (a) (i) 5   (ii) 8   (iii) 4
   (b) (i) 4   (ii) 6
   (c) (i) 30°   (ii) 150°
   (d) 24

2 (a) 38 cm^2 (b) $h = \dfrac{2A}{a+b}$

   (c) $a = \dfrac{2A}{h} - b$

3 (a) $19x + 8$
   (b) $10x^2 + 31x - 14$
   (c) $25x^2 - 20x + 4$
   (d) $12x^2 - 25x + 12$
4 (a) $x = 2$ (b) $x = 3$
   (c) $x = 4$ (d) $x = 15$
5 0.2 cm
6 67.3 m
7 (a) 9
   (b) (i) $\frac{1}{2}$ (ii) $\frac{1}{2}$ (iii) $\frac{3}{8}$ (iv) $\frac{1}{4}$
   (c) (i) $\frac{1}{64}$ (ii) $\frac{3}{64}$ (iii) 0
8 (a) $A(-3, 2)$, $B(2, 4)$
   (b)

(c) $D(-3, -2)$
(d) $E(2, 2)$
(e) $F(2, -2)$
(f) (i) 5 sq. units
    (ii) 20 sq. units
    (iii) 5 sq. units
    (iv) 30 sq. units

9 (a) 48.2°   (b) 89.4 m
   (c) 45.6 m
   (d) (i) 5614 m²
       (ii) 0.561 hectares

10 $\dfrac{(l + b)^2}{h}$ is a length.

$l^2 b$ is a volume; h is a length.
A volume and a length cannot be
added together

Revision Paper 17

1 (a) 0.066, 0.315, 0.33, 0.373
   (b) (i) 2.2 mm
       (ii) 0.54 m²
       (iii) 300 cm³
2 £112.50
3 £198
4 (a) 240 m   (b) 144 m²
5 (a) $15a^5$ (b) $27a^6$
   (c) 8   (d) $\frac{5}{6}$

6 (a) A, C, E
   (b) A, B, E
   (c) D
7 (a) 21   (b) 68
8 (a) 4.33 m   (b) 30°
   (c) 30°   (d) 7.66 m
   (e) 10.13 m
9 (a) Don (b) $\frac{1}{96}$ (c) $\frac{5}{8}$
10 361 m

Revision Paper 18

1 (a) (i) 3, 41   (ii) 16
   (b) 5, 8, 11, 14, 17
   (c) 78, 101
2 $x = 85°$
3 (a) $2x + 4$
   (b) (i) $12a^5$ (ii) $3a^3$
       (iii) $12a^5 b^6$
4 (a) 1. is cheapest
   (b) 2. is dearest
5 (a) 30 cm   (b) 10 cm
6 (a) $\frac{1}{10}$ (b) $\frac{1}{12}$
   (c) $\frac{33}{40}$ (d) 231
7 (a) Q   (b) P
8 (a) $A(-3, -1)$, $B(3, 5)$, $C(3, -1)$
   (b) (i) $y = -1$, (ii) $x = 3$
   (c) 1   (d) $y = x$

9 a trapezium, $1\frac{1}{2}$ sq. units
(a)

P	3	4	5	6	7
A	$\frac{1}{2}$	1	$1\frac{1}{2}$	2	$2\frac{1}{2}$

P	8	9	10	11	12
A	3	$3\frac{1}{2}$	4	$4\frac{1}{2}$	5

(b) $A = \frac{1}{2}(P - 2)$ (i) 9   (ii) 26
(c) $P = 2(A + 1)$
10 (a)

x	-2	-1.5	-1	1	2	3
$4x^2$	16	9	4	4	16	36

(b) ± 2.24
(c) -1.08 and 2.33

Revision Paper 19

1 (a) $a = 240\,000$ $b = 6000$
   (b) (i) 246 000   (ii) 234 000
   (c) 2.46×10^5, 2.34×10^5
2 57, 68
3 (a) 5   (b) 2   (c) 5
4 (a) (i) £5.88   (ii) 19.25 g
   (b) 24   (c) 2^{-2}
5 (a) DE = 4 cm, DF = 8 cm
   (b) 9 : 4
6 (a) $\frac{1}{3}$ (b) $\frac{2}{3}$ (c) $\frac{2}{9}$
7 $x = 17°$, $y = 99°$, $z = 227°$, 360°
8 (a) 9.8°C
   (b) 8.42 a.m. and p.m.

9 (a) B
   (b)

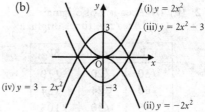

   (c) (i) A reflection in the x-axis
       (ii) A translation of 3 units up
            parallel to Oy
10 (a) (i) 9   (ii) 40%
   (b) (i) 4   (ii) 2

Revision Paper 20

1

Fraction	Decimal	Percentage
$\frac{1}{2}$	0.5	50%
$\frac{1}{4}$	0.25	25%
$\frac{4}{5}$	0.8	80%
$\frac{3}{4}$	0.75	75%

2 (a) (i) $x = -4$ or 7
       (ii) $x = 3$ or 4
   (b) (i) 37.5   (ii) 37.54   (iii) 38
3 (a) >   (b) =   (c) =   (d) <

9 (a) $\frac{1}{5}$ (b) $\frac{1}{2}$ (c) $\frac{2}{3}$
   (b)

		cassette	cassette	1st box disc	disc	disc
2nd box	cassette	(C, C)	(C, C)	(C, D)	(C, D)	(C, D)
	cassette	(C, C)	(C, C)	(C, D)	(C, D)	(C, D)
	cassette	(C, C)	(C, C)	(C, D)	(C, D)	(C, D)
	disc	(D, C)	(D, C)	(D, D)	(D, D)	(D, D)

       (i) 0.3   (ii) 0.15
10 (a) £471   (b) £30
   (c) £1592   (d) £1778
   (e) £145   (f) £2452.80

4 (a) 72°
   (b) $x = 90°$, $y = 108°$, $z = 72°$
5 (a) 4500   (b) 3000
6 (a) 70°   (b) 55°
   (c) (i) 250°   (ii) 305°
   (e) 7.52 km
7 (a) 250 km   (b) 5 h
   (c) 50 km/h
8 (a) (i)   area units
       (ii) volume units
       (iii) length units
   (b) (i) cm^2 (ii) cm
       (iii) cm^3 (iv) cm^2
   (c) (i), (iii) and (vi) are correct,
       (ii), (iv) and (v) incorrect

Revision Paper

21

1 1% (0.58%)

2 (b) (i) Area is $\frac{1}{4}$ of original
     (ii) Area is 4 times original

3

CP	Profit	SP
£50	£20	£70
£60	£24	£84
£75	£30	£105

4 (a) (i) 2 000 000 m^2
     (ii) 200 hectares
  (b) 1 : 2500

5 (a) 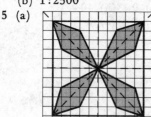 (b) $\frac{2}{5}$

6 (a) 16 mm
  (b) 18 cm
  (c) 9 cm
  (d) 12.5 m

7 (a) (i) 640 m^2 (ii) 88 m^2
  (b) 5 m
  (c) (i) 7.48 m   (ii) 56.3°
  (d) (i) 22.8 m   (ii) 20.6 m
     (iii) 13.6 m

8 (a) 7 and 8   (b) 7.72

9 (a) 1 h 49 min (b) 1 h 19 min
  (c) 1535, 1 h   (d) 3
  (e) 1000

10 (a) 8.19 m   (b) 6.87 m

Revision Paper

22

1 (a) 48   (b) 5   (c) 3
2 (a) $2^4 \times 3^4$ (b) 36
3 13.14 cm^2
4 (a) $3(x^2 + 3)$ (b) $3x(x + 3)$
  (c) $(x + 6)(x - 4)$
  (d) $(x + 3)(x - 3)$
5 (a) £360
  (b)

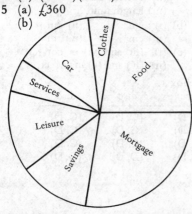

6 (a) £4899   (b) £4684.59
7 £472.88, 19.3%

8 (a) 11 cm^2 (b) 1.41 cm
  (c) 20 cm^2 (d) 16 cm^2

9 (a) triangular prism
  (b) (i) 5   (ii) 9   (iii) 6
  (c) (i) 6 cm^2 (ii) 12 cm^3
  (d)

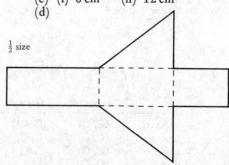

$\frac{1}{2}$ size

10 (a) Family size (family size costs
     0.36 p per g, bath costs 0.375 p
     per g and toilet costs 0.51 p
     per g)
  (b) Yes

Revision Paper

23

1 (a) £324   (b) £116.48
2 (a) (i) 684   (ii) £779.76
   (b) 65°F, 66°F or 67°F
3 (a) $a = 2$, $b = -7$, $c = -4$
   (b) $a = -5$, $b = 3$ or $a = 3$, $b = -5$
4 (a) +   (b) +   (c) −
   (d) uncorrelated
5 (a) 2.75%   (b) £5.46
6 AC = 11.9 cm
7 (a) £57 300
   (b) £62 600, each correct to nearest £100
8 (a)

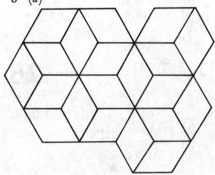

   (b) 60°, 120°, 60°, 120°

9 (a) (i) increase   (ii) increase
       (iii) constant
   (b) (i) 1994   (ii) 1991
   (c) (i) 27   (ii) 58

10

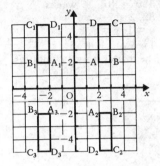

Revision Paper

24

1 (a) 4.83×10^8
   (b) (i) 5.2×10^{-6} (ii) 5.2×10^{-8}
2 (a) 8   (b) 7   (c) $7\frac{2}{3}$
3 (a) $\frac{1}{6}$
   (b) Profit − there should be 6 wins paying out 240p for every 36 punters paying 360p for their turns
   (c) 0   (d) $\frac{1}{2}$
4 £4396
5 (a) $x(6 - x)\,\text{m}^2$
   (c) When $x = 1$, $y = 1.3$ and when $x = 6$, $y = 6.3$
   (e) 1.36 m

6 (a)

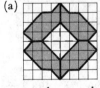

   (b) (i) $\frac{1}{2}$ (ii) $\frac{1}{2}$
7 (a) 70
8 (a) $\dfrac{800\pi}{3}\,\text{cm}^2$
   (b) 20π cm
9 £20 868, £6956
10 (a) 5.8 mm
   (b) 0.625 p
   (c) 0.814 p
   (d) 30%

279

Revision Paper $\qquad$ 25

1 (a) £52   (b) $\frac{3}{8}$ (c) 6
2 (a) $\frac{1}{3}$ (b) $\frac{4}{15}$ (c) 0
3 $4.15 \leqslant l < 4.25$, $2.45 \leqslant b < 2.55$, $10.84\,\text{m}^2$ (to 2 d.p.)
4 (a) 380   (b) 19 weeks
   (c) 82, 2
5 (a) $x = 1, y = 3, z = 2$
   (b) $1\frac{5}{7}$ (c) $4^2, 5^2, 2^5, 3^4$
6 No, she misses it by 12 minutes.
7 16, 5

8 (a), (c) and (e)

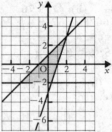

   (b) 3
   (d) $x = 2, y = 3$
9 (b) High correlation   (d) 14
10 (a) (i) 5.4 cm   (ii) 5.6 cm
   (b) $X\widehat{Y}Z = 90°$
   (c) Yes, $P\widehat{Q}R$ (d) 36.9°

Revision Paper $\qquad$ 26

1 (a) 5, 13, 17   (b) 5
   (c) 29, 33, 37
2 (a) 4.47 cm   (b) $89.44\,\text{cm}^3$
3 $34''$ nearer
4 (a) (i) $a(a - 5)$ (ii) $a(a + 7)$
      (iii) $ab(3a + 2b)$
   (b) (i) $\dfrac{11x}{8}$ (ii) $-\dfrac{x}{8}$ (iii) $\dfrac{5}{3}$
5 (a) (i) $n < 2$ (ii) $n < 3$
   (b) (i) 4   (ii) 4
6 (a) 13   (b)
   (c) (i)   (ii)
   (d) $36\,\text{cm}^2$ (e) 6
   (f) No
7 (a) 1248.5 mm   (b) 498.2 mm
8

$x = -3$

9 (a) (i) 051°   (ii) 231°   (iii) 141°
   (b) a right-angled triangle
   (c) 6.48 km (3 s.f.)
   (d) 5.03 km (3 s.f.)

10 (a) 39
   (b)

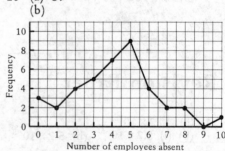

   (c) 4.2

(d)

Number of employees	0	1	2	3	4	5	6	7	8	9	10
Cumulative frequency	3	5	9	14	21	30	34	36	38	38	39

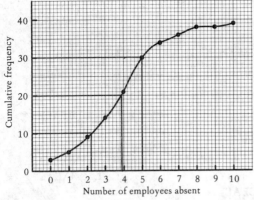

(e) 3.9, 2.8

Revision Paper 27

1 (a) 21 (b) $M = 4N - 3$
   (c) 5
2 (a) $a = 3$ (b) $b = 3$
   (c) $c = -5$ (d) $a = 30$
   (e) $x = -5$ or 9 (f) $x = -7$ or 4
3 (a) 2892.02 (b) 30p
4 (a) 41 years (b) 142
5 7.25, 0.458, 38.65; 38.192
6 (a) 2.4 m
   (b) (i) 0.565 m^2 (ii) 2.52 m^2
       (iii) 3.09 m^2
   (c) 185 m^3
7 (a) New coordinates are
       C(6, −2), D(6, 1)

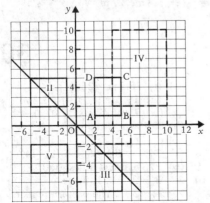

8 (a) ΔBEF, ΔCEF, ΔBCF, ΔBCE,
       ΔCED
   (b) CF, AB, CD (c) parallelogram
   (d) ΔABE (e) BCEF, BCDE
   (f) (i) reflection in BF
       (ii) rotation of 180° about X
       (iii) translation along FD
9 (a) 10 (b) 50
   (c) (i) 1020 h (ii) 1080 h, 950 h
       (iii) 130 h
   (d) Most have a life greater than
       900 h but less than 1100 h
10 (a) 1.27 m, 2.81 m, 4.52 m
    (b) 14.5 m (c) 29
    (d) 6.25 m^2

Revision Paper 28

1 (a) 2, 3, 5, 7, 11, 13, 17
  (b) 1, 2, 2, 4, 2, 4
  (c) (i) 23, 30   (ii) 271, 445
2 (a) (i) 8   (ii) −7
  (b) $q = p^2/9$
3 $m = 2, c = −5$
4 (a) (i) $6x^2 − 11x − 10$
      (ii) $6x^2 − 29x + 28$
      (iii) $16x^2 − 9$
  (b) (i) −2   (ii) $\frac{5}{4}$
5 (a) Incorrect dimensions for a volume
  (b) $V = \frac{2}{3}c(a^2 + b^2 + c^2)$ would be acceptable
6 (a) 5
  (b) (i) 72°   (ii) 54°   (iii) 108°
  (c) CDEA, CDEB, CBAD or CBAE

7 (a) 11   (b) 12
8 8.34 cm
9 (a) x cm, $(x − 7)$ cm, $(x − 3)$ cm
  (b) (i) 19 cm   (ii) 12 cm
10

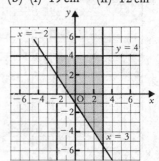

A trapezium

Revision Paper 29

1 (a)

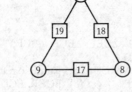

  (b)

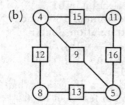

2 1, 0.948

3 (a) 74   (b) 602
4 (a) (i) $\frac{1}{72}$ (ii) $\frac{1}{24}$
  (b) all of them
5 (a) less, by £11   (b) £340, £4.50
6 (a) 21
  (b) the government won by 14 votes (324 to 310)

7 (a) 21   (b) 7   (c) 12
  (d) 6   (e) 1, 24   (f) £49.60
8 116 to 3 s.f.
9 (a) Freddy   (b) $\frac{1}{6}$
  (c) $\frac{1}{24}$ (d) $\frac{1}{3}$
  (e) (i) 120   (ii) 8
10 (a) $\dfrac{75}{x^2}$ (c)

3	5	6
109	85	86

  (e) 5.3 m, 2.7 m

Revision Paper 30

1 (a) 2×23^2 (b) £23
2 (a) £740   (b) 509 cm²
3 (a) (i) 65, 89, 117
      (ii) The first number is odd and all additions are even.
  (b) 2, 5, 9, 14, 20, 27
4 (a) 551 gal   (b) 163 cm
5 (a) 12:5:3   (b) 30 kg
  (c) 72 kg

6 (a) (i) 78.5 m² (25π)
      (ii) 19.6 m²   (iii) 12.5 m²
      (iv) 71.4 m²   (v) 7.07 m
  (b) 35 700 m³ (to 3 s. f.)
7 50 p
8 (a) 34°   (b) 68°   (c) 44°
9 (b) 176 nautical miles, 060°
10 2, −1, −3, −2, 1, 3,
   2, −1, −3 ... The pattern repeats